ISBN: 978-0-578-64651-0

Cover and book design by Stacy Bressler.
Licensed cover art and other watercolor style images by tatiana_troian via Creative Market
Licensed National Park artwork by Lemonade Pixel via Creative Market
Licensed doodle style images by Andimaginary Creative Co. via Creative Market

Stacy Bressler
P.O. Box 8904
Jackson, WY 83002
Email: hello@thecrazyoutdoormama.com
For more information on camping, go to thecrazyoutdoormama.com

HELLO CAMPER!

My name is Stacy Bressler, and I'm a married mama of three camp loving kids! We live in Jackson, Wyoming and have been on many a camp trip - and plan on going on many more!

I wanted to start documenting our trips, however wanted something as vibrant and beautiful as I felt our memories were. After browsing a couple of different places, I just couldn't find what I was looking for... so I made my own!

I hope you enjoy this less "work log" style of camping planner/journal and that you fill it with your own wonderful memories!

My passion is writing on my website, thecrazyoutdoormama.com, to give other families tons of tips and tricks to fully enjoy their camp life (especially with kids!) In fact, I have a pretty darn large selection of kids camping activities there!

Thank you so much for your purchase, and I wish you safe and happy travels!

All the best,
Stacy

P.S. Don't forget to head to the url below to join our community of campers ⟩⟩⟩ that journal too! You will also be the first to know about updates and giveaways!

Join the club at thecrazyoutdoormama.com/campsite-journal-friends/

YEAR AT A GLANCE

JANUARY

FEBRUARY

MARCH

APRIL

MAY

JUNE

JULY

AUGUST

SEPTEMBER

OCTOBER

NOVEMBER

DECEMBER

MY STORY... SO FAR

MEET MY RIG

PASTE A PICTURE OF YOUR CAMPER HERE!

MEET MY CREW

PASTE A PICTURE OF YOUR CAMP CREW HERE - PARTNER,
FAMILY, PET·· WHOEVER MAKES YOUR TRAVELS SPECIAL!

THE PLACES I'VE BEEN

CAMPSITE NAME   LOCATION   DATES STAYED

1

2

3

4

5

6

7

8

9

 I GOTTA GO DO THAT AGAIN!

THE PLACES I'VE BEEN

CAMPSITE NAME	LOCATION	DATES STAYED
10		
11		
12		
13		
14		
15		
16		
17		
18		

" I GOTTA GO DO THAT AGAIN! "

THE PLACES I'VE BEEN

CAMPSITE NAME   LOCATION   DATES STAYED

19

20

21

22

23

24

25

26

27

 I GOTTA GO DO THAT AGAIN!

8

THE PLACES I'VE BEEN

CAMPSITE NAME	LOCATION	DATES STAYED
28		
29		
30		
31		
32		
33		
34		
35		
36		

" I GOTTA GO DO THAT AGAIN! "

THE PLACES I'VE BEEN

CAMPSITE NAME	LOCATION	DATES STAYED
37		
38		
39		
40		
41		
42		
43		
44		
45		

" I GOTTA GO DO THAT AGAIN! "

THE PLACES I'VE BEEN

CAMPSITE NAME	LOCATION	DATES STAYED
46		
47		
48		
49		
50		
51		
52		
53		
54		

" I GOTTA GO DO THAT AGAIN! "

THE PLACES I'VE BEEN

CAMPSITE NAME	LOCATION	DATES STAYED
55		
56		
57		
58		
59		
60		
61		
62		
63		

" I GOTTA GO DO THAT AGAIN! "

THE PLACES I'VE BEEN

CAMPSITE NAME	LOCATION	DATES STAYED
64		
65		
66		
67		
68		
69		
70		
71		
72		

" I GOTTA GO DO THAT AGAIN! "

THE PLACES I'VE BEEN

CAMPSITE NAME	LOCATION	DATES STAYED
73		
74		
75		
76		
77		
78		
79		
80		
81		

" I GOTTA GO DO THAT AGAIN! "

STATES I'VE SEEN

WRITE IN THE DATE THAT YOU VISITED EACH STATE!

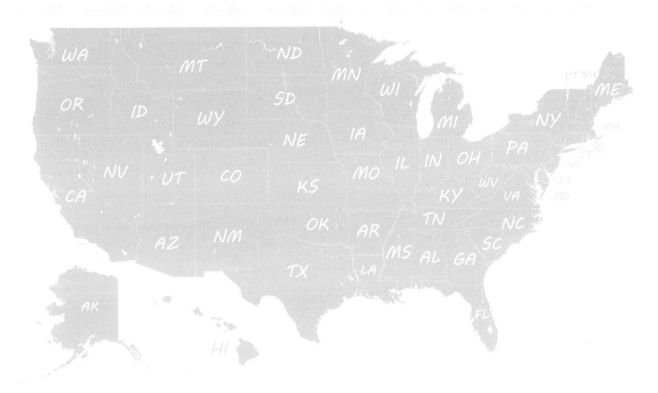

Alabama _____
Alaska _____
Arizona _____
Arkansas _____
California _____
Colorado _____
Connecticut _____
Delaware _____
Florida _____
Georgia _____
Hawaii _____
Idaho _____
Illinois _____
Indiana _____
Iowa _____
Kansas _____
Kentucky _____

Louisiana _____
Maine _____
Maryland _____
Massachusetts _____
Michigan _____
Minnesota _____
Mississippi _____
Missouri _____
Montana _____
Nebraska _____
Nevada _____
New Hampshire _____
New Jersey _____
New Mexico _____
New York _____
North Carolina _____
North Dakota _____

Ohio _____
Oklahoma _____
Oregon _____
Pennsylvania _____
Rhode Island _____
South Carolina _____
South Dakota _____
Tennessee _____
Texas _____
Utah _____
Vermont _____
Virginia _____
Washington _____
West Virginia _____
Wisconsin _____
Wyoming _____

NATIONAL PARKS

WRITE IN THE DATE THAT YOU VISITED EACH NATIONAL PARK

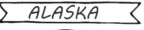

Date Visited _____

Date Visited _____

Date Visited _____

Date Visited _____

Date Visited _____

Date Visited _____

Date Visited _____

Date Visited _____

Date Visited _____

Date Visited _____

Date Visited _____

Date Visited _____

Date Visited _____

> AMERICAN SAMOA <

Date Visited _____

> ARKANSAS <

Date Visited _____

Date Visited _____

Date Visited _____

Date Visited _____

NATIONAL PARKS

CALIFORNIA CONT

Redwood
NATIONAL PARK

Date Visited _____

Mesa Verde
NATIONAL PARK

Date Visited _____

INDIANA

Channel Islands
NATIONAL PARK

Date Visited _____

Black Canyon
of the Gunnison
NATIONAL PARK

Date Visited _____

Sequoia
NATIONAL PARK

Date Visited _____

Great Sand
Dunes
NATIONAL PARK

Date Visited _____

Lassen Volcanic
NATIONAL PARK

Date Visited _____

COLORADO

Rocky Mountains
NATIONAL PARK

Date Visited _____

FLORIDA

Biscayne
NATIONAL PARK

Date Visited _____

Everglades
NATIONAL PARK

Date Visited _____

Dry Tortugas
NATIONAL PARK

Date Visited _____

HAWAII

Haleakala
NATIONAL PARK

Date Visited _____

Hawaii Volcanoes
NATIONAL PARK

Date Visited _____

KENTUCKY

Mammoth Cave
NATIONAL PARK

Date Visited _____

INDIANA

Indiana Dunes
NATIONAL PARK

Date Visited _____

MAINE

Acadia
NATIONAL PARK

Date Visited _____

MICHIGAN

Isle Royale
NATIONAL PARK

Date Visited _____

MINNESOTA

Voyageurs
NATIONAL PARK

Date Visited _____

NATIONAL PARKS

MISSOURI

Date Visited _____

NORTH DAKOTA

Date Visited _____

SOUTH CAROLINA

Date Visited _____

UTAH

Date Visited _____

MONTANA

Date Visited _____

NORTH CAROLINA

Date Visited _____

SOUTH DAKOTA

Date Visited _____

Date Visited _____

NEVADA

Date Visited _____

OHIO

Date Visited _____

Date Visited _____

TEXAS

Date Visited _____

Date Visited _____

Date Visited _____

NEW MEXICO

Date Visited _____

OREGON

Date Visited _____

Date Visited _____

Date Visited _____

NATIONAL PARKS

VIRGIN ISLANDS

Date Visited _____

Date Visited _____

VIRGINIA

Date Visited _____

WYOMING

Date Visited _____

WASHINGTON

Date Visited _____

Date Visited _____

Date Visited _____

OTHER NATIONAL PARKS AND SPECIAL PLACES I'VE SEEN

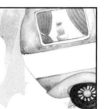

FRIENDS I'VE MADE

NAME	PHONE/EMAIL	WHERE/HOW I MET THEM
♡ _____	_____	_____
♡ _____	_____	_____
♡ _____	_____	_____
♡ _____	_____	_____
♡ _____	_____	_____
♡ _____	_____	_____
♡ _____	_____	_____
♡ _____	_____	_____
♡ _____	_____	_____
♡ _____	_____	_____
♡ _____	_____	_____
♡ _____	_____	_____
♡ _____	_____	_____
♡ _____	_____	_____
♡ _____	_____	_____
♡ _____	_____	_____

 # MY BUCKET LIST!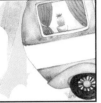

PICK YOUR TOP FOUR BUCKET LIST PLACES AND PASTE A PICTURE (AND ADD THE DATE!) IN THE CORRESPONDING BOX WHEN YOU REACH THEM!

DESTINATION

I MADE IT!

DATE

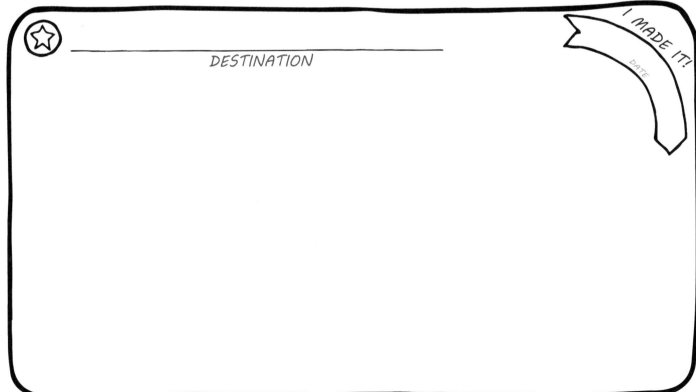

DESTINATION

I MADE IT!

DATE

MY BUCKET LIST!

PICK YOUR TOP FOUR BUCKET LIST PLACES AND PASTE A PICTURE (AND ADD THE DATE!) IN THE CORRESPONDING BOX WHEN YOU REACH THEM!

☆ _____
DESTINATION

I MADE IT!
DATE

☆ _____
DESTINATION

I MADE IT!
DATE

22

MY BUCKET LIST!

ADD ANYMORE BUCKET LIST DESTINATIONS HERE!

THE DREAM	I MADE IT!

☆ _____ DATE

☆ _____ DATE

☆ _____ DATE

☆ _____ DATE

☆ _____ DATE

☆ _____ DATE

☆ _____ DATE

☆ _____ DATE

☆ _____ DATE

☆ _____ DATE

☆ _____ DATE

☆ _____ DATE

CAMPGROUND DETAILS

CAMPGROUND NAME

⊗ LOCATION: _____

▭➜ DATES STAYED: _____

✳ SPOT NUMBER: _____

✿ AVG· TEMPS _____

COST PER NIGHT

☆ THE BEST SPOT # FOR NEXT TIME _____

›››››››› AMENITIES ‹‹‹‹‹‹‹‹

☐ WATER
☐ SEWER HOOKUPS
☐ DUMP STATION
☐ CELL SERVICE
☐ WIFI AVAILABLE
☐ 15 AMP
☐ 30 AMP

☐ RESTROOMS
☐ SHOWERS
☐ LAUNDRY
☐ GENERATORS ALLOWED?
☐ PETS ALLOWED?
☐ PICNIC TABLE
☐ FIREPIT

☐ STORE ON SITE
☐ WHEELCHAIR ACCESSIBLE
☐ GROUP SITES
☐ SHADE
☐ FLAT SITES
☐ PULL THROUGH
☐ TRAIL ACCESS

NEARBY ATTRACTIONS ⟶

CAMPGROUND NOTES

>>>>>>>>>>> MY FAVORITE MEMORY FROM THIS CAMP TRIP

NOTES TO REMEMBER FOR NEXT TIME

A PICTURE OR FUNNY STORY TO SMILE ABOUT LATER:

CAMPGROUND DETAILS

CAMPGROUND NAME

LOCATION: _____

DATES STAYED: _____

COST PER NIGHT

SPOT NUMBER: _____   AVG. TEMPS _____

THE BEST SPOT # FOR NEXT TIME _____

AMENITIES

- [ ] WATER
- [ ] SEWER HOOKUPS
- [ ] DUMP STATION
- [ ] CELL SERVICE
- [ ] WIFI AVAILABLE
- [ ] 15 AMP
- [ ] 30 AMP

- [ ] RESTROOMS
- [ ] SHOWERS
- [ ] LAUNDRY
- [ ] GENERATORS ALLOWED?
- [ ] PETS ALLOWED?
- [ ] PICNIC TABLE
- [ ] FIREPIT

- [ ] STORE ON SITE
- [ ] WHEELCHAIR ACCESSIBLE
- [ ] GROUP SITES
- [ ] SHADE
- [ ] FLAT SITES
- [ ] PULL THROUGH
- [ ] TRAIL ACCESS

NEARBY ATTRACTIONS

CAMPGROUND NOTES

 MY FAVORITE MEMORY FROM THIS CAMP TRIP

NOTES TO REMEMBER FOR NEXT TIME

A PICTURE OR FUNNY STORY TO SMILE ABOUT LATER:

CAMPGROUND DETAILS

CAMPGROUND NAME

ⓧ LOCATION: _____

⬒➡ DATES STAYED:_____

✳ SPOT NUMBER: _____

COST PER NIGHT

✤ AVG. TEMPS _____

☆ THE BEST SPOT # FOR NEXT TIME _____

▶▶▶▶▶▶▶ AMENITIES ◀◀◀◀◀◀◀

- ☐ WATER
- ☐ SEWER HOOKUPS
- ☐ DUMP STATION
- ☐ CELL SERVICE
- ☐ WIFI AVAILABLE
- ☐ 15 AMP
- ☐ 30 AMP

- ☐ RESTROOMS
- ☐ SHOWERS
- ☐ LAUNDRY
- ☐ GENERATORS ALLOWED?
- ☐ PETS ALLOWED?
- ☐ PICNIC TABLE
- ☐ FIREPIT

- ☐ STORE ON SITE
- ☐ WHEELCHAIR ACCESSIBLE
- ☐ GROUP SITES
- ☐ SHADE
- ☐ FLAT SITES
- ☐ PULL THROUGH
- ☐ TRAIL ACCESS

NEARBY ATTRACTIONS ⇨

CAMPGROUND NOTES

>>>>>>>>>> MY FAVORITE MEMORY FROM THIS CAMP TRIP

NOTES TO REMEMBER FOR NEXT TIME

A PICTURE OR FUNNY STORY TO SMILE ABOUT LATER:

CAMPGROUND DETAILS

CAMPGROUND NAME

(X) LOCATION: _____

COST PER NIGHT

[→] DATES STAYED: _____

(*) SPOT NUMBER: _____ (✿) AVG. TEMPS _____

(☆) THE BEST SPOT # FOR NEXT TIME _____

>>>>>>>> AMENITIES <<<<<<<<

☐ WATER
☐ SEWER HOOKUPS
☐ DUMP STATION
☐ CELL SERVICE
☐ WIFI AVAILABLE
☐ 15 AMP
☐ 30 AMP

☐ RESTROOMS
☐ SHOWERS
☐ LAUNDRY
☐ GENERATORS ALLOWED?
☐ PETS ALLOWED?
☐ PICNIC TABLE
☐ FIREPIT

☐ STORE ON SITE
☐ WHEELCHAIR ACCESSIBLE
☐ GROUP SITES
☐ SHADE
☐ FLAT SITES
☐ PULL THROUGH
☐ TRAIL ACCESS

NEARBY ATTRACTIONS ⤵

CAMPGROUND NOTES

>>>>>>>>>> MY FAVORITE MEMORY FROM THIS CAMP TRIP

NOTES TO REMEMBER FOR NEXT TIME

A PICTURE OR FUNNY STORY TO SMILE ABOUT LATER:

_____

_____

_____

_____

_____

_____

_____

_____

CAMPGROUND DETAILS

CAMPGROUND NAME

(x) LOCATION: _____

COST PER NIGHT

▢→ DATES STAYED: _____

✳ SPOT NUMBER: _____ ✿ AVG. TEMPS _____

☆ THE BEST SPOT # FOR NEXT TIME _____

⟫⟫⟫ AMENITIES ⟪⟪⟪

☐ WATER   ☐ RESTROOMS   ☐ STORE ON SITE
☐ SEWER HOOKUPS ☐ SHOWERS   ☐ WHEELCHAIR ACCESSIBLE
☐ DUMP STATION   ☐ LAUNDRY   ☐ GROUP SITES
☐ CELL SERVICE   ☐ GENERATORS ALLOWED? ☐ SHADE
☐ WIFI AVAILABLE ☐ PETS ALLOWED?   ☐ FLAT SITES
☐ 15 AMP   ☐ PICNIC TABLE   ☐ PULL THROUGH
☐ 30 AMP   ☐ FIREPIT   ☐ TRAIL ACCESS

NEARBY ATTRACTIONS ↬

CAMPGROUND NOTES

 MY FAVORITE MEMORY FROM THIS CAMP TRIP

NOTES TO REMEMBER FOR NEXT TIME

A PICTURE OR FUNNY STORY TO SMILE ABOUT LATER:

CAMPGROUND DETAILS

CAMPGROUND NAME

LOCATION: _____

DATES STAYED: _____

SPOT NUMBER: _____

COST PER NIGHT

✦ AVG. TEMPS _____

☆ THE BEST SPOT # FOR NEXT TIME _____

▶▶▶▶▶▶▶▶▶ AMENITIES ◀◀◀◀◀◀◀◀◀

- ☐ WATER
- ☐ SEWER HOOKUPS
- ☐ DUMP STATION
- ☐ CELL SERVICE
- ☐ WIFI AVAILABLE
- ☐ 15 AMP
- ☐ 30 AMP

- ☐ RESTROOMS
- ☐ SHOWERS
- ☐ LAUNDRY
- ☐ GENERATORS ALLOWED?
- ☐ PETS ALLOWED?
- ☐ PICNIC TABLE
- ☐ FIREPIT

- ☐ STORE ON SITE
- ☐ WHEELCHAIR ACCESSIBLE
- ☐ GROUP SITES
- ☐ SHADE
- ☐ FLAT SITES
- ☐ PULL THROUGH
- ☐ TRAIL ACCESS

NEARBY ATTRACTIONS ↠

CAMPGROUND NOTES

>>>>>>>>>>> MY FAVORITE MEMORY FROM THIS CAMP TRIP

NOTES TO REMEMBER FOR NEXT TIME

A PICTURE OR FUNNY STORY TO SMILE ABOUT LATER:

CAMPGROUND DETAILS

CAMPGROUND NAME

(×) LOCATION: _____

COST PER NIGHT

➡ DATES STAYED: _____

(✳) SPOT NUMBER: _____   AVG. TEMPS _____

(☆) THE BEST SPOT # FOR NEXT TIME _____

▶▶▶▶▶ AMENITIES ◀◀◀◀◀◀

- ☐ WATER
- ☐ SEWER HOOKUPS
- ☐ DUMP STATION
- ☐ CELL SERVICE
- ☐ WIFI AVAILABLE
- ☐ 15 AMP
- ☐ 30 AMP

- ☐ RESTROOMS
- ☐ SHOWERS
- ☐ LAUNDRY
- ☐ GENERATORS ALLOWED?
- ☐ PETS ALLOWED?
- ☐ PICNIC TABLE
- ☐ FIREPIT

- ☐ STORE ON SITE
- ☐ WHEELCHAIR ACCESSIBLE
- ☐ GROUP SITES
- ☐ SHADE
- ☐ FLAT SITES
- ☐ PULL THROUGH
- ☐ TRAIL ACCESS

NEARBY ATTRACTIONS ↣

CAMPGROUND NOTES

>>>>>>>>>>> MY FAVORITE MEMORY FROM THIS CAMP TRIP

NOTES TO REMEMBER FOR NEXT TIME

A PICTURE OR FUNNY STORY TO SMILE ABOUT LATER:

CAMPGROUND DETAILS

CAMPGROUND NAME

⊗ LOCATION: _____

↪ DATES STAYED: _____

✳ SPOT NUMBER: _____

⭐ THE BEST SPOT # FOR NEXT TIME _____

COST PER NIGHT

✤ AVG. TEMPS _____

▶▶▶▶▶▶ AMENITIES ◀◀◀◀◀◀

☐ WATER
☐ SEWER HOOKUPS
☐ DUMP STATION
☐ CELL SERVICE
☐ WIFI AVAILABLE
☐ 15 AMP
☐ 30 AMP

☐ RESTROOMS
☐ SHOWERS
☐ LAUNDRY
☐ GENERATORS ALLOWED?
☐ PETS ALLOWED?
☐ PICNIC TABLE
☐ FIREPIT

☐ STORE ON SITE
☐ WHEELCHAIR ACCESSIBLE
☐ GROUP SITES
☐ SHADE
☐ FLAT SITES
☐ PULL THROUGH
☐ TRAIL ACCESS

NEARBY ATTRACTIONS ↣↘

CAMPGROUND NOTES

>>>>>>>>>>> MY FAVORITE MEMORY FROM THIS CAMP TRIP

NOTES TO REMEMBER FOR NEXT TIME

A PICTURE OR FUNNY STORY TO SMILE ABOUT LATER:

CAMPGROUND DETAILS

CAMPGROUND NAME

(×) LOCATION: _____

➡ DATES STAYED: _____

COST PER NIGHT

(✳) SPOT NUMBER: _____ (✿) AVG. TEMPS _____

(☆) THE BEST SPOT # FOR NEXT TIME _____

▶▶▶▶▶ AMENITIES ◀◀◀◀◀

☐ WATER
☐ SEWER HOOKUPS
☐ DUMP STATION
☐ CELL SERVICE
☐ WIFI AVAILABLE
☐ 15 AMP
☐ 30 AMP

☐ RESTROOMS
☐ SHOWERS
☐ LAUNDRY
☐ GENERATORS ALLOWED?
☐ PETS ALLOWED?
☐ PICNIC TABLE
☐ FIREPIT

☐ STORE ON SITE
☐ WHEELCHAIR ACCESSIBLE
☐ GROUP SITES
☐ SHADE
☐ FLAT SITES
☐ PULL THROUGH
☐ TRAIL ACCESS

NEARBY ATTRACTIONS ↠

CAMPGROUND NOTES

>>>>>>>>>>> MY FAVORITE MEMORY FROM THIS CAMP TRIP

NOTES TO REMEMBER FOR NEXT TIME

A PICTURE OR FUNNY STORY TO SMILE ABOUT LATER:

CAMPGROUND DETAILS

CAMPGROUND NAME

⊗ LOCATION: _____

⇥ DATES STAYED: _____

✳ SPOT NUMBER: _____ ✤ AVG. TEMPS _____

☆ THE BEST SPOT # FOR NEXT TIME _____

COST PER NIGHT

⟫⟫⟫⟫ AMENITIES ⟪⟪⟪⟪

☐ WATER
☐ SEWER HOOKUPS
☐ DUMP STATION
☐ CELL SERVICE
☐ WIFI AVAILABLE
☐ 15 AMP
☐ 30 AMP

☐ RESTROOMS
☐ SHOWERS
☐ LAUNDRY
☐ GENERATORS ALLOWED?
☐ PETS ALLOWED?
☐ PICNIC TABLE
☐ FIREPIT

☐ STORE ON SITE
☐ WHEELCHAIR ACCESSIBLE
☐ GROUP SITES
☐ SHADE
☐ FLAT SITES
☐ PULL THROUGH
☐ TRAIL ACCESS

NEARBY ATTRACTIONS ⇢

CAMPGROUND NOTES

⫸⫸⫸⫸⫸ MY FAVORITE MEMORY FROM THIS CAMP TRIP

NOTES TO REMEMBER FOR NEXT TIME

A PICTURE OR FUNNY STORY TO SMILE ABOUT LATER:

CAMPGROUND DETAILS

CAMPGROUND NAME

(×) LOCATION: _____

▭➡ DATES STAYED: _____

✳ SPOT NUMBER: _____

✿ AVG. TEMPS _____

☆ THE BEST SPOT # FOR NEXT TIME _____

COST PER NIGHT

▶▶▶▶▶ AMENITIES ◀◀◀◀◀◀

☐ WATER
☐ SEWER HOOKUPS
☐ DUMP STATION
☐ CELL SERVICE
☐ WIFI AVAILABLE
☐ 15 AMP
☐ 30 AMP

☐ RESTROOMS
☐ SHOWERS
☐ LAUNDRY
☐ GENERATORS ALLOWED?
☐ PETS ALLOWED?
☐ PICNIC TABLE
☐ FIREPIT

☐ STORE ON SITE
☐ WHEELCHAIR ACCESSIBLE
☐ GROUP SITES
☐ SHADE
☐ FLAT SITES
☐ PULL THROUGH
☐ TRAIL ACCESS

NEARBY ATTRACTIONS ↗

CAMPGROUND NOTES

MY FAVORITE MEMORY FROM THIS CAMP TRIP

NOTES TO REMEMBER FOR NEXT TIME

A PICTURE OR FUNNY STORY TO SMILE ABOUT LATER:

CAMPGROUND DETAILS

CAMPGROUND NAME

(✗) LOCATION: _____

⬛➡ DATES STAYED: _____

(✳) SPOT NUMBER: _____ (✿) AVG. TEMPS _____

(☆) THE BEST SPOT # FOR NEXT TIME _____

COST PER NIGHT

▶▶▶▶▶▶ AMENITIES ◀◀◀◀◀◀

- ☐ WATER
- ☐ SEWER HOOKUPS
- ☐ DUMP STATION
- ☐ CELL SERVICE
- ☐ WIFI AVAILABLE
- ☐ 15 AMP
- ☐ 30 AMP

- ☐ RESTROOMS
- ☐ SHOWERS
- ☐ LAUNDRY
- ☐ GENERATORS ALLOWED?
- ☐ PETS ALLOWED?
- ☐ PICNIC TABLE
- ☐ FIREPIT

- ☐ STORE ON SITE
- ☐ WHEELCHAIR ACCESSIBLE
- ☐ GROUP SITES
- ☐ SHADE
- ☐ FLAT SITES
- ☐ PULL THROUGH
- ☐ TRAIL ACCESS

NEARBY ATTRACTIONS ↬

CAMPGROUND NOTES

>>>>>>>>>> MY FAVORITE MEMORY FROM THIS CAMP TRIP

NOTES TO REMEMBER FOR NEXT TIME

A PICTURE OR FUNNY STORY TO SMILE ABOUT LATER:

CAMPGROUND DETAILS

CAMPGROUND NAME

(✕) LOCATION: _____

↦ DATES STAYED: _____

(✳) SPOT NUMBER: _____

(✿) AVG. TEMPS _____

(★) THE BEST SPOT # FOR NEXT TIME _____

COST PER NIGHT

▶▶▶▶▶▶▶ AMENITIES ◀◀◀◀◀◀◀

- ☐ WATER
- ☐ SEWER HOOKUPS
- ☐ DUMP STATION
- ☐ CELL SERVICE
- ☐ WIFI AVAILABLE
- ☐ 15 AMP
- ☐ 30 AMP

- ☐ RESTROOMS
- ☐ SHOWERS
- ☐ LAUNDRY
- ☐ GENERATORS ALLOWED?
- ☐ PETS ALLOWED?
- ☐ PICNIC TABLE
- ☐ FIREPIT

- ☐ STORE ON SITE
- ☐ WHEELCHAIR ACCESSIBLE
- ☐ GROUP SITES
- ☐ SHADE
- ☐ FLAT SITES
- ☐ PULL THROUGH
- ☐ TRAIL ACCESS

NEARBY ATTRACTIONS ↘

CAMPGROUND NOTES

>>>>>>>>>> MY FAVORITE MEMORY FROM THIS CAMP TRIP

NOTES TO REMEMBER FOR NEXT TIME

A PICTURE OR FUNNY STORY TO SMILE ABOUT LATER:

CAMPGROUND DETAILS

CAMPGROUND NAME

LOCATION: _____

DATES STAYED: _____

SPOT NUMBER: _____

AVG. TEMPS _____

THE BEST SPOT # FOR NEXT TIME _____

COST PER NIGHT

>>>>>>> AMENITIES <<<<<<<

- ☐ WATER
- ☐ SEWER HOOKUPS
- ☐ DUMP STATION
- ☐ CELL SERVICE
- ☐ WIFI AVAILABLE
- ☐ 15 AMP
- ☐ 30 AMP

- ☐ RESTROOMS
- ☐ SHOWERS
- ☐ LAUNDRY
- ☐ GENERATORS ALLOWED?
- ☐ PETS ALLOWED?
- ☐ PICNIC TABLE
- ☐ FIREPIT

- ☐ STORE ON SITE
- ☐ WHEELCHAIR ACCESSIBLE
- ☐ GROUP SITES
- ☐ SHADE
- ☐ FLAT SITES
- ☐ PULL THROUGH
- ☐ TRAIL ACCESS

NEARBY ATTRACTIONS

CAMPGROUND NOTES

>>>>>>>>> MY FAVORITE MEMORY FROM THIS CAMP TRIP

NOTES TO REMEMBER FOR NEXT TIME

A PICTURE OR FUNNY STORY TO SMILE ABOUT LATER:

_____

_____

_____

_____

_____

_____

_____

_____

CAMPGROUND DETAILS

CAMPGROUND NAME

❌ LOCATION: _____

➡️ DATES STAYED: _____

✳️ SPOT NUMBER: _____ ✿ AVG. TEMPS _____

⭐ THE BEST SPOT # FOR NEXT TIME _____

COST PER NIGHT

AMENITIES

- ☐ WATER
- ☐ SEWER HOOKUPS
- ☐ DUMP STATION
- ☐ CELL SERVICE
- ☐ WIFI AVAILABLE
- ☐ 15 AMP
- ☐ 30 AMP

- ☐ RESTROOMS
- ☐ SHOWERS
- ☐ LAUNDRY
- ☐ GENERATORS ALLOWED?
- ☐ PETS ALLOWED?
- ☐ PICNIC TABLE
- ☐ FIREPIT

- ☐ STORE ON SITE
- ☐ WHEELCHAIR ACCESSIBLE
- ☐ GROUP SITES
- ☐ SHADE
- ☐ FLAT SITES
- ☐ PULL THROUGH
- ☐ TRAIL ACCESS

NEARBY ATTRACTIONS

CAMPGROUND NOTES

>>>>>>>>>>> MY FAVORITE MEMORY FROM THIS CAMP TRIP

NOTES TO REMEMBER FOR NEXT TIME

A PICTURE OR FUNNY STORY TO SMILE ABOUT LATER:

CAMPGROUND DETAILS

CAMPGROUND NAME

✕ LOCATION: _____

COST PER NIGHT

⬜➡ DATES STAYED: _____

✳ SPOT NUMBER: _____ ❁ AVG. TEMPS _____

⭐ THE BEST SPOT # FOR NEXT TIME _____

▸▸▸▸▸▸ AMENITIES ◂◂◂◂◂◂

- ☐ WATER
- ☐ SEWER HOOKUPS
- ☐ DUMP STATION
- ☐ CELL SERVICE
- ☐ WIFI AVAILABLE
- ☐ 15 AMP
- ☐ 30 AMP

- ☐ RESTROOMS
- ☐ SHOWERS
- ☐ LAUNDRY
- ☐ GENERATORS ALLOWED?
- ☐ PETS ALLOWED?
- ☐ PICNIC TABLE
- ☐ FIREPIT

- ☐ STORE ON SITE
- ☐ WHEELCHAIR ACCESSIBLE
- ☐ GROUP SITES
- ☐ SHADE
- ☐ FLAT SITES
- ☐ PULL THROUGH
- ☐ TRAIL ACCESS

NEARBY ATTRACTIONS ⤳

CAMPGROUND NOTES

>>>>>>>>>> MY FAVORITE MEMORY FROM THIS CAMP TRIP

NOTES TO REMEMBER FOR NEXT TIME

A PICTURE OR FUNNY STORY TO SMILE ABOUT LATER:

CAMPGROUND DETAILS

CAMPGROUND NAME

LOCATION: _____

COST PER NIGHT

DATES STAYED: _____

SPOT NUMBER: _____ **AVG. TEMPS** _____

THE BEST SPOT # FOR NEXT TIME _____

▶▶▶▶▶▶▶▶ AMENITIES ◀◀◀◀◀◀◀◀

- ☐ WATER
- ☐ SEWER HOOKUPS
- ☐ DUMP STATION
- ☐ CELL SERVICE
- ☐ WIFI AVAILABLE
- ☐ 15 AMP
- ☐ 30 AMP

- ☐ RESTROOMS
- ☐ SHOWERS
- ☐ LAUNDRY
- ☐ GENERATORS ALLOWED?
- ☐ PETS ALLOWED?
- ☐ PICNIC TABLE
- ☐ FIREPIT

- ☐ STORE ON SITE
- ☐ WHEELCHAIR ACCESSIBLE
- ☐ GROUP SITES
- ☐ SHADE
- ☐ FLAT SITES
- ☐ PULL THROUGH
- ☐ TRAIL ACCESS

NEARBY ATTRACTIONS ⇻

CAMPGROUND NOTES

>>>>>>>>>>> MY FAVORITE MEMORY FROM THIS CAMP TRIP

NOTES TO REMEMBER FOR NEXT TIME

A PICTURE OR FUNNY STORY TO SMILE ABOUT LATER:

CAMPGROUND DETAILS

CAMPGROUND NAME

LOCATION: _____

COST PER NIGHT

DATES STAYED: _____

SPOT NUMBER: _____ AVG. TEMPS _____

THE BEST SPOT # FOR NEXT TIME _____

►►►► AMENITIES ◄◄◄◄

☐ WATER
☐ SEWER HOOKUPS
☐ DUMP STATION
☐ CELL SERVICE
☐ WIFI AVAILABLE
☐ 15 AMP
☐ 30 AMP

☐ RESTROOMS
☐ SHOWERS
☐ LAUNDRY
☐ GENERATORS ALLOWED?
☐ PETS ALLOWED?
☐ PICNIC TABLE
☐ FIREPIT

☐ STORE ON SITE
☐ WHEELCHAIR ACCESSIBLE
☐ GROUP SITES
☐ SHADE
☐ FLAT SITES
☐ PULL THROUGH
☐ TRAIL ACCESS

NEARBY ATTRACTIONS

CAMPGROUND NOTES

>>>>>>>>>> MY FAVORITE MEMORY FROM THIS CAMP TRIP

NOTES TO REMEMBER FOR NEXT TIME

A PICTURE OR FUNNY STORY TO SMILE ABOUT LATER:

_____

_____

_____

_____

_____

_____

_____

_____

CAMPGROUND DETAILS

CAMPGROUND NAME

⊗ LOCATION: _____

⬜➡ DATES STAYED: _____

✳ SPOT NUMBER: _____

COST PER NIGHT

✿ AVG. TEMPS _____

⭐ THE BEST SPOT # FOR NEXT TIME _____

▶▶▶▶▶▶ AMENITIES ◀◀◀◀◀◀◀

☐ WATER
☐ SEWER HOOKUPS
☐ DUMP STATION
☐ CELL SERVICE
☐ WIFI AVAILABLE
☐ 15 AMP
☐ 30 AMP

☐ RESTROOMS
☐ SHOWERS
☐ LAUNDRY
☐ GENERATORS ALLOWED?
☐ PETS ALLOWED?
☐ PICNIC TABLE
☐ FIREPIT

☐ STORE ON SITE
☐ WHEELCHAIR ACCESSIBLE
☐ GROUP SITES
☐ SHADE
☐ FLAT SITES
☐ PULL THROUGH
☐ TRAIL ACCESS

NEARBY ATTRACTIONS ↬

CAMPGROUND NOTES

>>>>>>>>>> MY FAVORITE MEMORY FROM THIS CAMP TRIP

NOTES TO REMEMBER FOR NEXT TIME

A PICTURE OR FUNNY STORY TO SMILE ABOUT LATER:

CAMPGROUND DETAILS

CAMPGROUND NAME

X LOCATION: _____

↦ DATES STAYED: _____

COST PER NIGHT

✴ SPOT NUMBER: _____ **✦** AVG. TEMPS _____

☆ THE BEST SPOT # FOR NEXT TIME _____

▶▶▶▶▶▶ AMENITIES ◀◀◀◀◀◀◀

- ☐ WATER
- ☐ SEWER HOOKUPS
- ☐ DUMP STATION
- ☐ CELL SERVICE
- ☐ WIFI AVAILABLE
- ☐ 15 AMP
- ☐ 30 AMP

- ☐ RESTROOMS
- ☐ SHOWERS
- ☐ LAUNDRY
- ☐ GENERATORS ALLOWED?
- ☐ PETS ALLOWED?
- ☐ PICNIC TABLE
- ☐ FIREPIT

- ☐ STORE ON SITE
- ☐ WHEELCHAIR ACCESSIBLE
- ☐ GROUP SITES
- ☐ SHADE
- ☐ FLAT SITES
- ☐ PULL THROUGH
- ☐ TRAIL ACCESS

NEARBY ATTRACTIONS →

CAMPGROUND NOTES

>>>>>>>>>> MY FAVORITE MEMORY FROM THIS CAMP TRIP

NOTES TO REMEMBER FOR NEXT TIME

A PICTURE OR FUNNY STORY TO SMILE ABOUT LATER:

CAMPGROUND DETAILS

CAMPGROUND NAME

(x) LOCATION: _____

▢→ DATES STAYED: _____

COST PER NIGHT

(*) SPOT NUMBER: _____   (✤) AVG. TEMPS _____

(☆) THE BEST SPOT # FOR NEXT TIME _____

⟫⟫⟫⟫⟫ AMENITIES ⟪⟪⟪⟪⟪

- ☐ WATER
- ☐ SEWER HOOKUPS
- ☐ DUMP STATION
- ☐ CELL SERVICE
- ☐ WIFI AVAILABLE
- ☐ 15 AMP
- ☐ 30 AMP

- ☐ RESTROOMS
- ☐ SHOWERS
- ☐ LAUNDRY
- ☐ GENERATORS ALLOWED?
- ☐ PETS ALLOWED?
- ☐ PICNIC TABLE
- ☐ FIREPIT

- ☐ STORE ON SITE
- ☐ WHEELCHAIR ACCESSIBLE
- ☐ GROUP SITES
- ☐ SHADE
- ☐ FLAT SITES
- ☐ PULL THROUGH
- ☐ TRAIL ACCESS

NEARBY ATTRACTIONS ↝

CAMPGROUND NOTES

>>>>>>>>> MY FAVORITE MEMORY FROM THIS CAMP TRIP

NOTES TO REMEMBER FOR NEXT TIME

A PICTURE OR FUNNY STORY TO SMILE ABOUT LATER:

CAMPGROUND DETAILS

CAMPGROUND NAME

✖ LOCATION: _____

▢➡ DATES STAYED: _____

✳ SPOT NUMBER: _____

✿ AVG. TEMPS _____

☆ THE BEST SPOT # FOR NEXT TIME _____

COST PER NIGHT

▶▶▶▶▶▶ AMENITIES ◀◀◀◀◀◀◀

- ▢ WATER
- ▢ SEWER HOOKUPS
- ▢ DUMP STATION
- ▢ CELL SERVICE
- ▢ WIFI AVAILABLE
- ▢ 15 AMP
- ▢ 30 AMP

- ▢ RESTROOMS
- ▢ SHOWERS
- ▢ LAUNDRY
- ▢ GENERATORS ALLOWED?
- ▢ PETS ALLOWED?
- ▢ PICNIC TABLE
- ▢ FIREPIT

- ▢ STORE ON SITE
- ▢ WHEELCHAIR ACCESSIBLE
- ▢ GROUP SITES
- ▢ SHADE
- ▢ FLAT SITES
- ▢ PULL THROUGH
- ▢ TRAIL ACCESS

NEARBY ATTRACTIONS ↬

CAMPGROUND NOTES

>>>>>>>>>>> MY FAVORITE MEMORY FROM THIS CAMP TRIP

NOTES TO REMEMBER FOR NEXT TIME

A PICTURE OR FUNNY STORY TO SMILE ABOUT LATER:

CAMPGROUND DETAILS

CAMPGROUND NAME

(×) LOCATION: _____

▭→ DATES STAYED: _____

✳ SPOT NUMBER: _____

☆ THE BEST SPOT # FOR NEXT TIME _____

COST PER NIGHT

✤ AVG. TEMPS _____

▶▶▶▶▶▶ AMENITIES ◀◀◀◀◀◀

- ☐ WATER
- ☐ SEWER HOOKUPS
- ☐ DUMP STATION
- ☐ CELL SERVICE
- ☐ WIFI AVAILABLE
- ☐ 15 AMP
- ☐ 30 AMP

- ☐ RESTROOMS
- ☐ SHOWERS
- ☐ LAUNDRY
- ☐ GENERATORS ALLOWED?
- ☐ PETS ALLOWED?
- ☐ PICNIC TABLE
- ☐ FIREPIT

- ☐ STORE ON SITE
- ☐ WHEELCHAIR ACCESSIBLE
- ☐ GROUP SITES
- ☐ SHADE
- ☐ FLAT SITES
- ☐ PULL THROUGH
- ☐ TRAIL ACCESS

NEARBY ATTRACTIONS �↘

CAMPGROUND NOTES

>>>>>>>>>>>>>> MY FAVORITE MEMORY FROM THIS CAMP TRIP

NOTES TO REMEMBER FOR NEXT TIME

A PICTURE OR FUNNY STORY TO SMILE ABOUT LATER:

CAMPGROUND DETAILS

CAMPGROUND NAME

⊗ LOCATION: _____

▭➡ DATES STAYED: _____

❋ SPOT NUMBER: _____

COST PER NIGHT

✦ AVG. TEMPS _____

☆ THE BEST SPOT # FOR NEXT TIME _____

▶▶▶▶▶ AMENITIES ◀◀◀◀◀

- ☐ WATER
- ☐ SEWER HOOKUPS
- ☐ DUMP STATION
- ☐ CELL SERVICE
- ☐ WIFI AVAILABLE
- ☐ 15 AMP
- ☐ 30 AMP

- ☐ RESTROOMS
- ☐ SHOWERS
- ☐ LAUNDRY
- ☐ GENERATORS ALLOWED?
- ☐ PETS ALLOWED?
- ☐ PICNIC TABLE
- ☐ FIREPIT

- ☐ STORE ON SITE
- ☐ WHEELCHAIR ACCESSIBLE
- ☐ GROUP SITES
- ☐ SHADE
- ☐ FLAT SITES
- ☐ PULL THROUGH
- ☐ TRAIL ACCESS

NEARBY ATTRACTIONS ↠

CAMPGROUND NOTES

⟫⟫⟫⟫⟫⟫ MY FAVORITE MEMORY FROM THIS CAMP TRIP

NOTES TO REMEMBER FOR NEXT TIME

A PICTURE OR FUNNY STORY TO SMILE ABOUT LATER:

CAMPGROUND DETAILS

CAMPGROUND NAME

❌ LOCATION: _____

➡️ DATES STAYED: _____

✳️ SPOT NUMBER: _____

✿ AVG. TEMPS _____

⭐ THE BEST SPOT # FOR NEXT TIME _____

COST PER NIGHT

▶▶▶▶▶▶ AMENITIES ◀◀◀◀◀◀

☐ WATER
☐ SEWER HOOKUPS
☐ DUMP STATION
☐ CELL SERVICE
☐ WIFI AVAILABLE
☐ 15 AMP
☐ 30 AMP

☐ RESTROOMS
☐ SHOWERS
☐ LAUNDRY
☐ GENERATORS ALLOWED?
☐ PETS ALLOWED?
☐ PICNIC TABLE
☐ FIREPIT

☐ STORE ON SITE
☐ WHEELCHAIR ACCESSIBLE
☐ GROUP SITES
☐ SHADE
☐ FLAT SITES
☐ PULL THROUGH
☐ TRAIL ACCESS

NEARBY ATTRACTIONS ⇸

CAMPGROUND NOTES

>>>>>>>>>> *MY FAVORITE MEMORY FROM THIS CAMP TRIP*

NOTES TO REMEMBER FOR NEXT TIME

A PICTURE OR FUNNY STORY TO SMILE ABOUT LATER:

CAMPGROUND DETAILS

CAMPGROUND NAME

LOCATION: _____

DATES STAYED: _____

SPOT NUMBER: _____

COST PER NIGHT

AVG. TEMPS _____

THE BEST SPOT # FOR NEXT TIME _____

▶▶▶▶ AMENITIES ◀◀◀◀

- ☐ WATER
- ☐ SEWER HOOKUPS
- ☐ DUMP STATION
- ☐ CELL SERVICE
- ☐ WIFI AVAILABLE
- ☐ 15 AMP
- ☐ 30 AMP

- ☐ RESTROOMS
- ☐ SHOWERS
- ☐ LAUNDRY
- ☐ GENERATORS ALLOWED?
- ☐ PETS ALLOWED?
- ☐ PICNIC TABLE
- ☐ FIREPIT

- ☐ STORE ON SITE
- ☐ WHEELCHAIR ACCESSIBLE
- ☐ GROUP SITES
- ☐ SHADE
- ☐ FLAT SITES
- ☐ PULL THROUGH
- ☐ TRAIL ACCESS

NEARBY ATTRACTIONS

CAMPGROUND NOTES

>>>>>>>>>>>> MY FAVORITE MEMORY FROM THIS CAMP TRIP

NOTES TO REMEMBER FOR NEXT TIME

A PICTURE OR FUNNY STORY TO SMILE ABOUT LATER:

CAMPGROUND DETAILS

CAMPGROUND NAME

LOCATION: _____

COST PER NIGHT

DATES STAYED: _____

SPOT NUMBER: _____   AVG. TEMPS _____

THE BEST SPOT # FOR NEXT TIME _____

AMENITIES

☐ WATER
☐ SEWER HOOKUPS
☐ DUMP STATION
☐ CELL SERVICE
☐ WIFI AVAILABLE
☐ 15 AMP
☐ 30 AMP

☐ RESTROOMS
☐ SHOWERS
☐ LAUNDRY
☐ GENERATORS ALLOWED?
☐ PETS ALLOWED?
☐ PICNIC TABLE
☐ FIREPIT

☐ STORE ON SITE
☐ WHEELCHAIR ACCESSIBLE
☐ GROUP SITES
☐ SHADE
☐ FLAT SITES
☐ PULL THROUGH
☐ TRAIL ACCESS

NEARBY ATTRACTIONS

CAMPGROUND NOTES

>>>>>>>>>> MY FAVORITE MEMORY FROM THIS CAMP TRIP

NOTES TO REMEMBER FOR NEXT TIME

A PICTURE OR FUNNY STORY TO SMILE ABOUT LATER:

CAMPGROUND DETAILS

CAMPGROUND NAME

(✗) LOCATION: _____

[→] DATES STAYED:_____

COST PER NIGHT

(✳) SPOT NUMBER:_____ (✿) AVG. TEMPS _____

(☆) THE BEST SPOT # FOR NEXT TIME _____

AMENITIES

- ☐ WATER
- ☐ SEWER HOOKUPS
- ☐ DUMP STATION
- ☐ CELL SERVICE
- ☐ WIFI AVAILABLE
- ☐ 15 AMP
- ☐ 30 AMP

- ☐ RESTROOMS
- ☐ SHOWERS
- ☐ LAUNDRY
- ☐ GENERATORS ALLOWED?
- ☐ PETS ALLOWED?
- ☐ PICNIC TABLE
- ☐ FIREPIT

- ☐ STORE ON SITE
- ☐ WHEELCHAIR ACCESSIBLE
- ☐ GROUP SITES
- ☐ SHADE
- ☐ FLAT SITES
- ☐ PULL THROUGH
- ☐ TRAIL ACCESS

NEARBY ATTRACTIONS ↝

CAMPGROUND NOTES

>>>>>>>>> MY FAVORITE MEMORY FROM THIS CAMP TRIP

NOTES TO REMEMBER FOR NEXT TIME

A PICTURE OR FUNNY STORY TO SMILE ABOUT LATER:

CAMPGROUND DETAILS

CAMPGROUND NAME

(X) LOCATION: _____

☐→ DATES STAYED: _____

COST PER NIGHT

(✳) SPOT NUMBER: _____ (✿) AVG. TEMPS _____

(☆) THE BEST SPOT # FOR NEXT TIME _____

⟫⟫⟫⟫ AMENITIES ⟪⟪⟪⟪

☐ WATER   ☐ RESTROOMS   ☐ STORE ON SITE
☐ SEWER HOOKUPS ☐ SHOWERS   ☐ WHEELCHAIR ACCESSIBLE
☐ DUMP STATION   ☐ LAUNDRY   ☐ GROUP SITES
☐ CELL SERVICE   ☐ GENERATORS ALLOWED? ☐ SHADE
☐ WIFI AVAILABLE ☐ PETS ALLOWED?   ☐ FLAT SITES
☐ 15 AMP   ☐ PICNIC TABLE   ☐ PULL THROUGH
☐ 30 AMP   ☐ FIREPIT   ☐ TRAIL ACCESS

NEARBY ATTRACTIONS ⤳

CAMPGROUND NOTES

>>>>>>>>>>> MY FAVORITE MEMORY FROM THIS CAMP TRIP

NOTES TO REMEMBER FOR NEXT TIME

A PICTURE OR FUNNY STORY TO SMILE ABOUT LATER:

CAMPGROUND DETAILS

CAMPGROUND NAME

LOCATION: _____

COST PER NIGHT

DATES STAYED: _____

SPOT NUMBER: _____   **AVG. TEMPS** _____

THE BEST SPOT # FOR NEXT TIME _____

>>>>>>>> AMENITIES <<<<<<<<

- ☐ WATER
- ☐ SEWER HOOKUPS
- ☐ DUMP STATION
- ☐ CELL SERVICE
- ☐ WIFI AVAILABLE
- ☐ 15 AMP
- ☐ 30 AMP

- ☐ RESTROOMS
- ☐ SHOWERS
- ☐ LAUNDRY
- ☐ GENERATORS ALLOWED?
- ☐ PETS ALLOWED?
- ☐ PICNIC TABLE
- ☐ FIREPIT

- ☐ STORE ON SITE
- ☐ WHEELCHAIR ACCESSIBLE
- ☐ GROUP SITES
- ☐ SHADE
- ☐ FLAT SITES
- ☐ PULL THROUGH
- ☐ TRAIL ACCESS

NEARBY ATTRACTIONS

CAMPGROUND NOTES

>>>>>>>>>> MY FAVORITE MEMORY FROM THIS CAMP TRIP

NOTES TO REMEMBER FOR NEXT TIME

A PICTURE OR FUNNY STORY TO SMILE ABOUT LATER:

_____

_____

_____

_____

_____

_____

_____

_____

CAMPGROUND DETAILS

CAMPGROUND NAME

⊗ LOCATION: _____

▭➡ DATES STAYED: _____

✳ SPOT NUMBER: _____

COST PER NIGHT

✤ AVG. TEMPS _____

☆ THE BEST SPOT # FOR NEXT TIME _____

⟫⟫⟫⟫ AMENITIES ⟪⟪⟪⟪

- ☐ WATER
- ☐ SEWER HOOKUPS
- ☐ DUMP STATION
- ☐ CELL SERVICE
- ☐ WIFI AVAILABLE
- ☐ 15 AMP
- ☐ 30 AMP

- ☐ RESTROOMS
- ☐ SHOWERS
- ☐ LAUNDRY
- ☐ GENERATORS ALLOWED?
- ☐ PETS ALLOWED?
- ☐ PICNIC TABLE
- ☐ FIREPIT

- ☐ STORE ON SITE
- ☐ WHEELCHAIR ACCESSIBLE
- ☐ GROUP SITES
- ☐ SHADE
- ☐ FLAT SITES
- ☐ PULL THROUGH
- ☐ TRAIL ACCESS

NEARBY ATTRACTIONS ↬

CAMPGROUND NOTES

>>>>>>>>>> MY FAVORITE MEMORY FROM THIS CAMP TRIP

NOTES TO REMEMBER FOR NEXT TIME

A PICTURE OR FUNNY STORY TO SMILE ABOUT LATER:

CAMPGROUND DETAILS

CAMPGROUND NAME

(×) LOCATION: _____

☐→ DATES STAYED: _____

(✳) SPOT NUMBER: _____   (✤) AVG. TEMPS _____

(☆) THE BEST SPOT # FOR NEXT TIME _____

COST PER NIGHT

►►►►►►►► AMENITIES ◄◄◄◄◄◄◄◄

☐ WATER
☐ SEWER HOOKUPS
☐ DUMP STATION
☐ CELL SERVICE
☐ WIFI AVAILABLE
☐ 15 AMP
☐ 30 AMP

☐ RESTROOMS
☐ SHOWERS
☐ LAUNDRY
☐ GENERATORS ALLOWED?
☐ PETS ALLOWED?
☐ PICNIC TABLE
☐ FIREPIT

☐ STORE ON SITE
☐ WHEELCHAIR ACCESSIBLE
☐ GROUP SITES
☐ SHADE
☐ FLAT SITES
☐ PULL THROUGH
☐ TRAIL ACCESS

NEARBY ATTRACTIONS ↠↘

CAMPGROUND NOTES

>>>>>>>>>>> MY FAVORITE MEMORY FROM THIS CAMP TRIP

NOTES TO REMEMBER FOR NEXT TIME

A PICTURE OR FUNNY STORY TO SMILE ABOUT LATER:

CAMPGROUND DETAILS

CAMPGROUND NAME

(X) LOCATION: _____

☐→ DATES STAYED: _____

COST PER NIGHT

(✳) SPOT NUMBER: _____ (✿) AVG. TEMPS _____

(☆) THE BEST SPOT # FOR NEXT TIME _____

≫≫≫≫≫ AMENITIES ≪≪≪≪≪

☐ WATER
☐ SEWER HOOKUPS
☐ DUMP STATION
☐ CELL SERVICE
☐ WIFI AVAILABLE
☐ 15 AMP
☐ 30 AMP

☐ RESTROOMS
☐ SHOWERS
☐ LAUNDRY
☐ GENERATORS ALLOWED?
☐ PETS ALLOWED?
☐ PICNIC TABLE
☐ FIREPIT

☐ STORE ON SITE
☐ WHEELCHAIR ACCESSIBLE
☐ GROUP SITES
☐ SHADE
☐ FLAT SITES
☐ PULL THROUGH
☐ TRAIL ACCESS

NEARBY ATTRACTIONS ⇝

CAMPGROUND NOTES

>>>>>>>>>>> MY FAVORITE MEMORY FROM THIS CAMP TRIP

NOTES TO REMEMBER FOR NEXT TIME

A PICTURE OR FUNNY STORY TO SMILE ABOUT LATER:

CAMPGROUND DETAILS

CAMPGROUND NAME

(X) LOCATION: _____

➡ DATES STAYED: _____

COST PER NIGHT

✳ SPOT NUMBER: _____

✿ AVG· TEMPS _____

☆ THE BEST SPOT # FOR NEXT TIME _____

▶▶▶▶▶ AMENITIES ◀◀◀◀◀

- ☐ WATER
- ☐ SEWER HOOKUPS
- ☐ DUMP STATION
- ☐ CELL SERVICE
- ☐ WIFI AVAILABLE
- ☐ 15 AMP
- ☐ 30 AMP

- ☐ RESTROOMS
- ☐ SHOWERS
- ☐ LAUNDRY
- ☐ GENERATORS ALLOWED?
- ☐ PETS ALLOWED?
- ☐ PICNIC TABLE
- ☐ FIREPIT

- ☐ STORE ON SITE
- ☐ WHEELCHAIR ACCESSIBLE
- ☐ GROUP SITES
- ☐ SHADE
- ☐ FLAT SITES
- ☐ PULL THROUGH
- ☐ TRAIL ACCESS

NEARBY ATTRACTIONS ↘

CAMPGROUND NOTES

>>>>>>>> MY FAVORITE MEMORY FROM THIS CAMP TRIP

NOTES TO REMEMBER FOR NEXT TIME

A PICTURE OR FUNNY STORY TO SMILE ABOUT LATER:

CAMPGROUND DETAILS

CAMPGROUND NAME

ⓧ LOCATION: _____

➡️ DATES STAYED: _____

✳️ SPOT NUMBER: _____

☆ THE BEST SPOT # FOR NEXT TIME _____

COST PER NIGHT

✤ AVG. TEMPS _____

AMENITIES

- ☐ WATER
- ☐ SEWER HOOKUPS
- ☐ DUMP STATION
- ☐ CELL SERVICE
- ☐ WIFI AVAILABLE
- ☐ 15 AMP
- ☐ 30 AMP

- ☐ RESTROOMS
- ☐ SHOWERS
- ☐ LAUNDRY
- ☐ GENERATORS ALLOWED?
- ☐ PETS ALLOWED?
- ☐ PICNIC TABLE
- ☐ FIREPIT

- ☐ STORE ON SITE
- ☐ WHEELCHAIR ACCESSIBLE
- ☐ GROUP SITES
- ☐ SHADE
- ☐ FLAT SITES
- ☐ PULL THROUGH
- ☐ TRAIL ACCESS

NEARBY ATTRACTIONS

CAMPGROUND NOTES

>>>>>>>>>>> MY FAVORITE MEMORY FROM THIS CAMP TRIP

NOTES TO REMEMBER FOR NEXT TIME

A PICTURE OR FUNNY STORY TO SMILE ABOUT LATER:

CAMPGROUND DETAILS

CAMPGROUND NAME

LOCATION: _____

DATES STAYED: _____

COST PER NIGHT

SPOT NUMBER: _____

AVG. TEMPS _____

THE BEST SPOT # FOR NEXT TIME _____

AMENITIES

- ☐ WATER
- ☐ SEWER HOOKUPS
- ☐ DUMP STATION
- ☐ CELL SERVICE
- ☐ WIFI AVAILABLE
- ☐ 15 AMP
- ☐ 30 AMP

- ☐ RESTROOMS
- ☐ SHOWERS
- ☐ LAUNDRY
- ☐ GENERATORS ALLOWED?
- ☐ PETS ALLOWED?
- ☐ PICNIC TABLE
- ☐ FIREPIT

- ☐ STORE ON SITE
- ☐ WHEELCHAIR ACCESSIBLE
- ☐ GROUP SITES
- ☐ SHADE
- ☐ FLAT SITES
- ☐ PULL THROUGH
- ☐ TRAIL ACCESS

NEARBY ATTRACTIONS

CAMPGROUND NOTES

>>>>>>>>>> *MY FAVORITE MEMORY FROM THIS CAMP TRIP*

NOTES TO REMEMBER FOR NEXT TIME

A PICTURE OR FUNNY STORY TO SMILE ABOUT LATER:

CAMPGROUND DETAILS

CAMPGROUND NAME

✕ LOCATION: _____

⇥ DATES STAYED: _____

✳ SPOT NUMBER: _____

COST PER NIGHT

✿ AVG. TEMPS _____

☆ THE BEST SPOT # FOR NEXT TIME _____

▶▶▶▶▶▶▶ AMENITIES ◀◀◀◀◀◀◀

☐ WATER
☐ SEWER HOOKUPS
☐ DUMP STATION
☐ CELL SERVICE
☐ WIFI AVAILABLE
☐ 15 AMP
☐ 30 AMP

☐ RESTROOMS
☐ SHOWERS
☐ LAUNDRY
☐ GENERATORS ALLOWED?
☐ PETS ALLOWED?
☐ PICNIC TABLE
☐ FIREPIT

☐ STORE ON SITE
☐ WHEELCHAIR ACCESSIBLE
☐ GROUP SITES
☐ SHADE
☐ FLAT SITES
☐ PULL THROUGH
☐ TRAIL ACCESS

NEARBY ATTRACTIONS ↠↘

CAMPGROUND NOTES

>>>>>>>>>> MY FAVORITE MEMORY FROM THIS CAMP TRIP

NOTES TO REMEMBER FOR NEXT TIME

A PICTURE OR FUNNY STORY TO SMILE ABOUT LATER:

CAMPGROUND DETAILS

CAMPGROUND NAME

(x) LOCATION: _____

➡ DATES STAYED: _____

COST PER NIGHT

(*) SPOT NUMBER: _____ ✦ AVG. TEMPS _____

(☆) THE BEST SPOT # FOR NEXT TIME _____

AMENITIES

☐ WATER
☐ SEWER HOOKUPS
☐ DUMP STATION
☐ CELL SERVICE
☐ WIFI AVAILABLE
☐ 15 AMP
☐ 30 AMP

☐ RESTROOMS
☐ SHOWERS
☐ LAUNDRY
☐ GENERATORS ALLOWED?
☐ PETS ALLOWED?
☐ PICNIC TABLE
☐ FIREPIT

☐ STORE ON SITE
☐ WHEELCHAIR ACCESSIBLE
☐ GROUP SITES
☐ SHADE
☐ FLAT SITES
☐ PULL THROUGH
☐ TRAIL ACCESS

NEARBY ATTRACTIONS ⇌

CAMPGROUND NOTES

>>>>>>>>>> MY FAVORITE MEMORY FROM THIS CAMP TRIP

NOTES TO REMEMBER FOR NEXT TIME

A PICTURE OR FUNNY STORY TO SMILE ABOUT LATER:

_____

_____

_____

_____

_____

_____

_____

_____

CAMPGROUND DETAILS

CAMPGROUND NAME

(×) LOCATION: _____

➡ DATES STAYED: _____

✳ SPOT NUMBER: _____

❁ AVG. TEMPS _____

☆ THE BEST SPOT # FOR NEXT TIME _____

COST PER NIGHT

▶▶▶▶▶▶ AMENITIES ◀◀◀◀◀◀◀

- ☐ WATER
- ☐ SEWER HOOKUPS
- ☐ DUMP STATION
- ☐ CELL SERVICE
- ☐ WIFI AVAILABLE
- ☐ 15 AMP
- ☐ 30 AMP

- ☐ RESTROOMS
- ☐ SHOWERS
- ☐ LAUNDRY
- ☐ GENERATORS ALLOWED?
- ☐ PETS ALLOWED?
- ☐ PICNIC TABLE
- ☐ FIREPIT

- ☐ STORE ON SITE
- ☐ WHEELCHAIR ACCESSIBLE
- ☐ GROUP SITES
- ☐ SHADE
- ☐ FLAT SITES
- ☐ PULL THROUGH
- ☐ TRAIL ACCESS

NEARBY ATTRACTIONS ⇾

CAMPGROUND NOTES

>>>>>>>>>> MY FAVORITE MEMORY FROM THIS CAMP TRIP

NOTES TO REMEMBER FOR NEXT TIME

A PICTURE OR FUNNY STORY TO SMILE ABOUT LATER:

CAMPGROUND DETAILS

CAMPGROUND NAME

⊗ LOCATION: _____

▭→ DATES STAYED: _____

✳ SPOT NUMBER: _____   ❀ AVG. TEMPS _____

COST PER NIGHT

☆ THE BEST SPOT # FOR NEXT TIME _____

▶▶▶▶▶ AMENITIES ◀◀◀◀◀

- ☐ WATER
- ☐ SEWER HOOKUPS
- ☐ DUMP STATION
- ☐ CELL SERVICE
- ☐ WIFI AVAILABLE
- ☐ 15 AMP
- ☐ 30 AMP

- ☐ RESTROOMS
- ☐ SHOWERS
- ☐ LAUNDRY
- ☐ GENERATORS ALLOWED?
- ☐ PETS ALLOWED?
- ☐ PICNIC TABLE
- ☐ FIREPIT

- ☐ STORE ON SITE
- ☐ WHEELCHAIR ACCESSIBLE
- ☐ GROUP SITES
- ☐ SHADE
- ☐ FLAT SITES
- ☐ PULL THROUGH
- ☐ TRAIL ACCESS

NEARBY ATTRACTIONS ↬

CAMPGROUND NOTES

>>>>>>>>>>> MY FAVORITE MEMORY FROM THIS CAMP TRIP

NOTES TO REMEMBER FOR NEXT TIME

A PICTURE OR FUNNY STORY TO SMILE ABOUT LATER:

CAMPGROUND DETAILS

CAMPGROUND NAME

⊗ LOCATION: _____

▢→ DATES STAYED: _____

✳ SPOT NUMBER: _____   ❂ AVG. TEMPS _____

☆ THE BEST SPOT # FOR NEXT TIME _____

COST PER NIGHT

⟫⟫⟫⟫ AMENITIES ⟪⟪⟪⟪

☐ WATER
☐ SEWER HOOKUPS
☐ DUMP STATION
☐ CELL SERVICE
☐ WIFI AVAILABLE
☐ 15 AMP
☐ 30 AMP

☐ RESTROOMS
☐ SHOWERS
☐ LAUNDRY
☐ GENERATORS ALLOWED?
☐ PETS ALLOWED?
☐ PICNIC TABLE
☐ FIREPIT

☐ STORE ON SITE
☐ WHEELCHAIR ACCESSIBLE
☐ GROUP SITES
☐ SHADE
☐ FLAT SITES
☐ PULL THROUGH
☐ TRAIL ACCESS

NEARBY ATTRACTIONS ↬

CAMPGROUND NOTES

>>>>>>>>>>> *MY FAVORITE MEMORY FROM THIS CAMP TRIP*

NOTES TO REMEMBER FOR NEXT TIME

A PICTURE OR FUNNY STORY TO SMILE ABOUT LATER:

CAMPGROUND DETAILS

CAMPGROUND NAME

LOCATION: _____

COST PER NIGHT

DATES STAYED: _____

SPOT NUMBER: _____ AVG. TEMPS _____

THE BEST SPOT # FOR NEXT TIME _____

AMENITIES

- ☐ WATER
- ☐ SEWER HOOKUPS
- ☐ DUMP STATION
- ☐ CELL SERVICE
- ☐ WIFI AVAILABLE
- ☐ 15 AMP
- ☐ 30 AMP

- ☐ RESTROOMS
- ☐ SHOWERS
- ☐ LAUNDRY
- ☐ GENERATORS ALLOWED?
- ☐ PETS ALLOWED?
- ☐ PICNIC TABLE
- ☐ FIREPIT

- ☐ STORE ON SITE
- ☐ WHEELCHAIR ACCESSIBLE
- ☐ GROUP SITES
- ☐ SHADE
- ☐ FLAT SITES
- ☐ PULL THROUGH
- ☐ TRAIL ACCESS

NEARBY ATTRACTIONS

CAMPGROUND NOTES

>>>>>>>>>>> *MY FAVORITE MEMORY FROM THIS CAMP TRIP*

NOTES TO REMEMBER FOR NEXT TIME

A PICTURE OR FUNNY STORY TO SMILE ABOUT LATER:

CAMPGROUND DETAILS

CAMPGROUND NAME

LOCATION: ____________________

DATES STAYED: ____________________

COST PER NIGHT

SPOT NUMBER: ____________

AVG. TEMPS __________

THE BEST SPOT # FOR NEXT TIME __________________

AMENITIES

- [ ] WATER
- [ ] SEWER HOOKUPS
- [ ] DUMP STATION
- [ ] CELL SERVICE
- [ ] WIFI AVAILABLE
- [ ] 15 AMP
- [ ] 30 AMP
- [ ] RESTROOMS
- [ ] SHOWERS
- [ ] LAUNDRY
- [ ] GENERATORS ALLOWED?
- [ ] PETS ALLOWED?
- [ ] PICNIC TABLE
- [ ] FIREPIT
- [ ] STORE ON SITE
- [ ] WHEELCHAIR ACCESSIBLE
- [ ] GROUP SITES
- [ ] SHADE
- [ ] FLAT SITES
- [ ] PULL THROUGH
- [ ] TRAIL ACCESS

NEARBY ATTRACTIONS

CAMPGROUND NOTES

>>>>>>>>>> *MY FAVORITE MEMORY FROM THIS CAMP TRIP*

NOTES TO REMEMBER FOR NEXT TIME

A PICTURE OR FUNNY STORY TO SMILE ABOUT LATER:

CAMPGROUND DETAILS

CAMPGROUND NAME

✖ LOCATION: _____

⬛➡ DATES STAYED: _____

✳ SPOT NUMBER: _____   ✿ AVG. TEMPS _____

COST PER NIGHT

☆ THE BEST SPOT # FOR NEXT TIME _____

▶▶▶▶▶▶▶ AMENITIES ◀◀◀◀◀◀◀

☐ WATER   ☐ RESTROOMS   ☐ STORE ON SITE
☐ SEWER HOOKUPS   ☐ SHOWERS   ☐ WHEELCHAIR ACCESSIBLE
☐ DUMP STATION   ☐ LAUNDRY   ☐ GROUP SITES
☐ CELL SERVICE   ☐ GENERATORS ALLOWED? ☐ SHADE
☐ WIFI AVAILABLE   ☐ PETS ALLOWED?   ☐ FLAT SITES
☐ 15 AMP   ☐ PICNIC TABLE   ☐ PULL THROUGH
☐ 30 AMP   ☐ FIREPIT   ☐ TRAIL ACCESS

NEARBY ATTRACTIONS ⤳

CAMPGROUND NOTES

>>>>>>>>>> MY FAVORITE MEMORY FROM THIS CAMP TRIP

NOTES TO REMEMBER FOR NEXT TIME

A PICTURE OR FUNNY STORY TO SMILE ABOUT LATER:

CAMPGROUND DETAILS

CAMPGROUND NAME

(x) LOCATION: _____

➡ DATES STAYED: _____

❋ SPOT NUMBER: _____

COST PER NIGHT

✿ AVG. TEMPS _____

☆ THE BEST SPOT # FOR NEXT TIME _____

▸▸▸▸▸▸▸▸▸ AMENITIES ◂◂◂◂◂◂◂◂◂

☐ WATER
☐ SEWER HOOKUPS
☐ DUMP STATION
☐ CELL SERVICE
☐ WIFI AVAILABLE
☐ 15 AMP
☐ 30 AMP

☐ RESTROOMS
☐ SHOWERS
☐ LAUNDRY
☐ GENERATORS ALLOWED?
☐ PETS ALLOWED?
☐ PICNIC TABLE
☐ FIREPIT

☐ STORE ON SITE
☐ WHEELCHAIR ACCESSIBLE
☐ GROUP SITES
☐ SHADE
☐ FLAT SITES
☐ PULL THROUGH
☐ TRAIL ACCESS

NEARBY ATTRACTIONS ↗

CAMPGROUND NOTES

>>>>>>>>>>>> MY FAVORITE MEMORY FROM THIS CAMP TRIP

NOTES TO REMEMBER FOR NEXT TIME

A PICTURE OR FUNNY STORY TO SMILE ABOUT LATER:

CAMPGROUND DETAILS

CAMPGROUND NAME

⊗ LOCATION: _____

▭➡ DATES STAYED: _____

✳ SPOT NUMBER: _____

✿ AVG. TEMPS _____

☆ THE BEST SPOT # FOR NEXT TIME _____

COST PER NIGHT

⟫⟫⟫⟫⟫⟫ AMENITIES ⟪⟪⟪⟪⟪⟪

☐ WATER
☐ SEWER HOOKUPS
☐ DUMP STATION
☐ CELL SERVICE
☐ WIFI AVAILABLE
☐ 15 AMP
☐ 30 AMP

☐ RESTROOMS
☐ SHOWERS
☐ LAUNDRY
☐ GENERATORS ALLOWED?
☐ PETS ALLOWED?
☐ PICNIC TABLE
☐ FIREPIT

☐ STORE ON SITE
☐ WHEELCHAIR ACCESSIBLE
☐ GROUP SITES
☐ SHADE
☐ FLAT SITES
☐ PULL THROUGH
☐ TRAIL ACCESS

NEARBY ATTRACTIONS ⤳

CAMPGROUND NOTES

>>>>>>>>>>> MY FAVORITE MEMORY FROM THIS CAMP TRIP

NOTES TO REMEMBER FOR NEXT TIME

A PICTURE OR FUNNY STORY TO SMILE ABOUT LATER:

CAMPGROUND DETAILS

CAMPGROUND NAME

LOCATION: _____

COST PER NIGHT

DATES STAYED: _____

SPOT NUMBER: _____   AVG. TEMPS _____

THE BEST SPOT # FOR NEXT TIME _____

>>>>>>>>> AMENITIES <<<<<<<<<

- ☐ WATER
- ☐ SEWER HOOKUPS
- ☐ DUMP STATION
- ☐ CELL SERVICE
- ☐ WIFI AVAILABLE
- ☐ 15 AMP
- ☐ 30 AMP

- ☐ RESTROOMS
- ☐ SHOWERS
- ☐ LAUNDRY
- ☐ GENERATORS ALLOWED?
- ☐ PETS ALLOWED?
- ☐ PICNIC TABLE
- ☐ FIREPIT

- ☐ STORE ON SITE
- ☐ WHEELCHAIR ACCESSIBLE
- ☐ GROUP SITES
- ☐ SHADE
- ☐ FLAT SITES
- ☐ PULL THROUGH
- ☐ TRAIL ACCESS

NEARBY ATTRACTIONS →

CAMPGROUND NOTES

>>>>>>>>>> MY FAVORITE MEMORY FROM THIS CAMP TRIP

NOTES TO REMEMBER FOR NEXT TIME

A PICTURE OR FUNNY STORY TO SMILE ABOUT LATER:

CAMPGROUND DETAILS

CAMPGROUND NAME

⊗ LOCATION: _____

☐→ DATES STAYED: _____

✳ SPOT NUMBER: _____

COST PER NIGHT

✾ AVG. TEMPS _____

☆ THE BEST SPOT # FOR NEXT TIME _____

▶▶▶▶▶▶ AMENITIES ◀◀◀◀◀◀

☐ WATER
☐ SEWER HOOKUPS
☐ DUMP STATION
☐ CELL SERVICE
☐ WIFI AVAILABLE
☐ 15 AMP
☐ 30 AMP

☐ RESTROOMS
☐ SHOWERS
☐ LAUNDRY
☐ GENERATORS ALLOWED?
☐ PETS ALLOWED?
☐ PICNIC TABLE
☐ FIREPIT

☐ STORE ON SITE
☐ WHEELCHAIR ACCESSIBLE
☐ GROUP SITES
☐ SHADE
☐ FLAT SITES
☐ PULL THROUGH
☐ TRAIL ACCESS

NEARBY ATTRACTIONS ↠

CAMPGROUND NOTES

>>>>>>>>>>> MY FAVORITE MEMORY FROM THIS CAMP TRIP

NOTES TO REMEMBER FOR NEXT TIME

A PICTURE OR FUNNY STORY TO SMILE ABOUT LATER:

CAMPGROUND DETAILS

CAMPGROUND NAME

⊗ LOCATION: _____

▣➡ DATES STAYED: _____

✳ SPOT NUMBER: _____

✪ THE BEST SPOT # FOR NEXT TIME _____

COST PER NIGHT

✿ AVG. TEMPS _____

▶▶▶▶▶▶ AMENITIES ◀◀◀◀◀◀◀

- ☐ WATER
- ☐ SEWER HOOKUPS
- ☐ DUMP STATION
- ☐ CELL SERVICE
- ☐ WIFI AVAILABLE
- ☐ 15 AMP
- ☐ 30 AMP

- ☐ RESTROOMS
- ☐ SHOWERS
- ☐ LAUNDRY
- ☐ GENERATORS ALLOWED?
- ☐ PETS ALLOWED?
- ☐ PICNIC TABLE
- ☐ FIREPIT

- ☐ STORE ON SITE
- ☐ WHEELCHAIR ACCESSIBLE
- ☐ GROUP SITES
- ☐ SHADE
- ☐ FLAT SITES
- ☐ PULL THROUGH
- ☐ TRAIL ACCESS

NEARBY ATTRACTIONS ⇻

CAMPGROUND NOTES

>>>>>>>>> MY FAVORITE MEMORY FROM THIS CAMP TRIP

NOTES TO REMEMBER FOR NEXT TIME

A PICTURE OR FUNNY STORY TO SMILE ABOUT LATER:

_____

_____

_____

_____

_____

_____

_____

_____

CAMPGROUND DETAILS

CAMPGROUND NAME

(×) LOCATION: _____

➡ DATES STAYED: _____

(✳) SPOT NUMBER: _____   (✤) AVG. TEMPS _____

(☆) THE BEST SPOT # FOR NEXT TIME _____

COST PER NIGHT

▶▶▶▶▶▶ AMENITIES ◀◀◀◀◀◀

☐ WATER   ☐ RESTROOMS   ☐ STORE ON SITE
☐ SEWER HOOKUPS   ☐ SHOWERS   ☐ WHEELCHAIR ACCESSIBLE
☐ DUMP STATION   ☐ LAUNDRY   ☐ GROUP SITES
☐ CELL SERVICE   ☐ GENERATORS ALLOWED? ☐ SHADE
☐ WIFI AVAILABLE   ☐ PETS ALLOWED?   ☐ FLAT SITES
☐ 15 AMP   ☐ PICNIC TABLE   ☐ PULL THROUGH
☐ 30 AMP   ☐ FIREPIT   ☐ TRAIL ACCESS

NEARBY ATTRACTIONS ⇥↘

CAMPGROUND NOTES

>>>>>>>>>> MY FAVORITE MEMORY FROM THIS CAMP TRIP

NOTES TO REMEMBER FOR NEXT TIME

A PICTURE OR FUNNY STORY TO SMILE ABOUT LATER:

_____

_____

_____

_____

_____

_____

_____

_____

CAMPGROUND DETAILS

CAMPGROUND NAME

LOCATION: _____

COST PER NIGHT

DATES STAYED: _____

SPOT NUMBER: _____ AVG. TEMPS _____

THE BEST SPOT # FOR NEXT TIME _____

>>>>>>> AMENITIES <<<<<<<

- ☐ WATER
- ☐ SEWER HOOKUPS
- ☐ DUMP STATION
- ☐ CELL SERVICE
- ☐ WIFI AVAILABLE
- ☐ 15 AMP
- ☐ 30 AMP

- ☐ RESTROOMS
- ☐ SHOWERS
- ☐ LAUNDRY
- ☐ GENERATORS ALLOWED?
- ☐ PETS ALLOWED?
- ☐ PICNIC TABLE
- ☐ FIREPIT

- ☐ STORE ON SITE
- ☐ WHEELCHAIR ACCESSIBLE
- ☐ GROUP SITES
- ☐ SHADE
- ☐ FLAT SITES
- ☐ PULL THROUGH
- ☐ TRAIL ACCESS

NEARBY ATTRACTIONS

CAMPGROUND NOTES

>>>>>>>>>> MY FAVORITE MEMORY FROM THIS CAMP TRIP

NOTES TO REMEMBER FOR NEXT TIME

A PICTURE OR FUNNY STORY TO SMILE ABOUT LATER:

_____
_____
_____
_____
_____
_____
_____
_____
_____

CAMPGROUND DETAILS

CAMPGROUND NAME

✗ LOCATION: _____

⬛➡ DATES STAYED: _____

✳ SPOT NUMBER: _____

✤ AVG. TEMPS _____

⭐ THE BEST SPOT # FOR NEXT TIME _____

COST PER NIGHT

▶▶▶▶▶▶ AMENITIES ◀◀◀◀◀◀

☐ WATER
☐ SEWER HOOKUPS
☐ DUMP STATION
☐ CELL SERVICE
☐ WIFI AVAILABLE
☐ 15 AMP
☐ 30 AMP

☐ RESTROOMS
☐ SHOWERS
☐ LAUNDRY
☐ GENERATORS ALLOWED?
☐ PETS ALLOWED?
☐ PICNIC TABLE
☐ FIREPIT

☐ STORE ON SITE
☐ WHEELCHAIR ACCESSIBLE
☐ GROUP SITES
☐ SHADE
☐ FLAT SITES
☐ PULL THROUGH
☐ TRAIL ACCESS

NEARBY ATTRACTIONS ⇒

CAMPGROUND NOTES

>>>>>>>>>> *MY FAVORITE MEMORY FROM THIS CAMP TRIP*

NOTES TO REMEMBER FOR NEXT TIME

A PICTURE OR FUNNY STORY TO SMILE ABOUT LATER:

CAMPGROUND DETAILS

CAMPGROUND NAME

LOCATION: _____

COST PER NIGHT

DATES STAYED: _____

SPOT NUMBER: _____   AVG. TEMPS _____

THE BEST SPOT # FOR NEXT TIME _____

⟫⟫⟫⟫ AMENITIES ⟪⟪⟪⟪

☐ WATER   ☐ RESTROOMS   ☐ STORE ON SITE
☐ SEWER HOOKUPS   ☐ SHOWERS   ☐ WHEELCHAIR ACCESSIBLE
☐ DUMP STATION   ☐ LAUNDRY   ☐ GROUP SITES
☐ CELL SERVICE   ☐ GENERATORS ALLOWED? ☐ SHADE
☐ WIFI AVAILABLE   ☐ PETS ALLOWED?   ☐ FLAT SITES
☐ 15 AMP   ☐ PICNIC TABLE   ☐ PULL THROUGH
☐ 30 AMP   ☐ FIREPIT   ☐ TRAIL ACCESS

NEARBY ATTRACTIONS ⤳

CAMPGROUND NOTES

>>>>>>>>>>> MY FAVORITE MEMORY FROM THIS CAMP TRIP

NOTES TO REMEMBER FOR NEXT TIME

A PICTURE OR FUNNY STORY TO SMILE ABOUT LATER:

_____

_____

_____

_____

_____

_____

_____

_____

CAMPGROUND DETAILS

CAMPGROUND NAME

(×) LOCATION: _____

➡ DATES STAYED: _____

✳ SPOT NUMBER: _____

⚘ AVG. TEMPS _____

☆ THE BEST SPOT # FOR NEXT TIME _____

COST PER NIGHT

▶▶▶▶▶▶▶ AMENITIES ◀◀◀◀◀◀◀◀

☐ WATER
☐ SEWER HOOKUPS
☐ DUMP STATION
☐ CELL SERVICE
☐ WIFI AVAILABLE
☐ 15 AMP
☐ 30 AMP

☐ RESTROOMS
☐ SHOWERS
☐ LAUNDRY
☐ GENERATORS ALLOWED?
☐ PETS ALLOWED?
☐ PICNIC TABLE
☐ FIREPIT

☐ STORE ON SITE
☐ WHEELCHAIR ACCESSIBLE
☐ GROUP SITES
☐ SHADE
☐ FLAT SITES
☐ PULL THROUGH
☐ TRAIL ACCESS

NEARBY ATTRACTIONS ⤳

CAMPGROUND NOTES

MY FAVORITE MEMORY FROM THIS CAMP TRIP

NOTES TO REMEMBER FOR NEXT TIME

A PICTURE OR FUNNY STORY TO SMILE ABOUT LATER:

CAMPGROUND DETAILS

CAMPGROUND NAME

✕ LOCATION: _____

⬛➡ DATES STAYED: _____

✴ SPOT NUMBER: _____

COST PER NIGHT

✧ AVG. TEMPS _____

☆ THE BEST SPOT # FOR NEXT TIME _____

▶▶▶▶▶▶▶ AMENITIES ◀◀◀◀◀◀◀

☐ WATER
☐ SEWER HOOKUPS
☐ DUMP STATION
☐ CELL SERVICE
☐ WIFI AVAILABLE
☐ 15 AMP
☐ 30 AMP

☐ RESTROOMS
☐ SHOWERS
☐ LAUNDRY
☐ GENERATORS ALLOWED?
☐ PETS ALLOWED?
☐ PICNIC TABLE
☐ FIREPIT

☐ STORE ON SITE
☐ WHEELCHAIR ACCESSIBLE
☐ GROUP SITES
☐ SHADE
☐ FLAT SITES
☐ PULL THROUGH
☐ TRAIL ACCESS

NEARBY ATTRACTIONS ➤

CAMPGROUND NOTES

>>>>>>>>>> MY FAVORITE MEMORY FROM THIS CAMP TRIP

NOTES TO REMEMBER FOR NEXT TIME

A PICTURE OR FUNNY STORY TO SMILE ABOUT LATER:

CAMPGROUND DETAILS

CAMPGROUND NAME

⊗ LOCATION: _____

▭➡ DATES STAYED: _____

✳ SPOT NUMBER: _____

☆ THE BEST SPOT # FOR NEXT TIME _____

COST PER NIGHT

✿ AVG. TEMPS _____

▶▶▶▶▶ AMENITIES ◀◀◀◀◀

- ☐ WATER
- ☐ SEWER HOOKUPS
- ☐ DUMP STATION
- ☐ CELL SERVICE
- ☐ WIFI AVAILABLE
- ☐ 15 AMP
- ☐ 30 AMP

- ☐ RESTROOMS
- ☐ SHOWERS
- ☐ LAUNDRY
- ☐ GENERATORS ALLOWED?
- ☐ PETS ALLOWED?
- ☐ PICNIC TABLE
- ☐ FIREPIT

- ☐ STORE ON SITE
- ☐ WHEELCHAIR ACCESSIBLE
- ☐ GROUP SITES
- ☐ SHADE
- ☐ FLAT SITES
- ☐ PULL THROUGH
- ☐ TRAIL ACCESS

NEARBY ATTRACTIONS ↬↘

CAMPGROUND NOTES

>>>>>>>> MY FAVORITE MEMORY FROM THIS CAMP TRIP

NOTES TO REMEMBER FOR NEXT TIME

A PICTURE OR FUNNY STORY TO SMILE ABOUT LATER:

CAMPGROUND DETAILS

CAMPGROUND NAME

$\otimes$ LOCATION: _____

COST PER NIGHT

$\rightarrow$ DATES STAYED: _____

$\ast$ SPOT NUMBER: _____ $\circledast$ AVG. TEMPS _____

$\star$ THE BEST SPOT # FOR NEXT TIME _____

AMENITIES

- ☐ WATER
- ☐ SEWER HOOKUPS
- ☐ DUMP STATION
- ☐ CELL SERVICE
- ☐ WIFI AVAILABLE
- ☐ 15 AMP
- ☐ 30 AMP

- ☐ RESTROOMS
- ☐ SHOWERS
- ☐ LAUNDRY
- ☐ GENERATORS ALLOWED?
- ☐ PETS ALLOWED?
- ☐ PICNIC TABLE
- ☐ FIREPIT

- ☐ STORE ON SITE
- ☐ WHEELCHAIR ACCESSIBLE
- ☐ GROUP SITES
- ☐ SHADE
- ☐ FLAT SITES
- ☐ PULL THROUGH
- ☐ TRAIL ACCESS

NEARBY ATTRACTIONS

CAMPGROUND NOTES

>>>>>>>>>>>> MY FAVORITE MEMORY FROM THIS CAMP TRIP

NOTES TO REMEMBER FOR NEXT TIME

A PICTURE OR FUNNY STORY TO SMILE ABOUT LATER:

CAMPGROUND DETAILS

CAMPGROUND NAME

✕ LOCATION: _____

➡ DATES STAYED: _____

✳ SPOT NUMBER: _____

☆ THE BEST SPOT # FOR NEXT TIME _____

COST PER NIGHT

✧ AVG. TEMPS _____

▶▶▶▶▶▶▶▶ AMENITIES ◀◀◀◀◀◀◀◀

- ☐ WATER
- ☐ SEWER HOOKUPS
- ☐ DUMP STATION
- ☐ CELL SERVICE
- ☐ WIFI AVAILABLE
- ☐ 15 AMP
- ☐ 30 AMP

- ☐ RESTROOMS
- ☐ SHOWERS
- ☐ LAUNDRY
- ☐ GENERATORS ALLOWED?
- ☐ PETS ALLOWED?
- ☐ PICNIC TABLE
- ☐ FIREPIT

- ☐ STORE ON SITE
- ☐ WHEELCHAIR ACCESSIBLE
- ☐ GROUP SITES
- ☐ SHADE
- ☐ FLAT SITES
- ☐ PULL THROUGH
- ☐ TRAIL ACCESS

NEARBY ATTRACTIONS ➢

CAMPGROUND NOTES

>>>>>>>>>> MY FAVORITE MEMORY FROM THIS CAMP TRIP

NOTES TO REMEMBER FOR NEXT TIME

A PICTURE OR FUNNY STORY TO SMILE ABOUT LATER:

_____

_____

_____

_____

_____

_____

_____

_____

CAMPGROUND DETAILS

CAMPGROUND NAME

(×) LOCATION: _____

↪ DATES STAYED: _____

✳ SPOT NUMBER: _____

COST PER NIGHT

✤ AVG. TEMPS _____

☆ THE BEST SPOT # FOR NEXT TIME _____

AMENITIES

☐ WATER
☐ SEWER HOOKUPS
☐ DUMP STATION
☐ CELL SERVICE
☐ WIFI AVAILABLE
☐ 15 AMP
☐ 30 AMP

☐ RESTROOMS
☐ SHOWERS
☐ LAUNDRY
☐ GENERATORS ALLOWED?
☐ PETS ALLOWED?
☐ PICNIC TABLE
☐ FIREPIT

☐ STORE ON SITE
☐ WHEELCHAIR ACCESSIBLE
☐ GROUP SITES
☐ SHADE
☐ FLAT SITES
☐ PULL THROUGH
☐ TRAIL ACCESS

NEARBY ATTRACTIONS ⇒

CAMPGROUND NOTES

>>>>>>>>>>> MY FAVORITE MEMORY FROM THIS CAMP TRIP

NOTES TO REMEMBER FOR NEXT TIME

A PICTURE OR FUNNY STORY TO SMILE ABOUT LATER:

CAMPGROUND DETAILS

CAMPGROUND NAME

LOCATION: ____________________

COST PER NIGHT

DATES STAYED: ____________________

SPOT NUMBER: ____________

AVG. TEMPS __________

THE BEST SPOT # FOR NEXT TIME ____________________

AMENITIES

- [ ] WATER
- [ ] SEWER HOOKUPS
- [ ] DUMP STATION
- [ ] CELL SERVICE
- [ ] WIFI AVAILABLE
- [ ] 15 AMP
- [ ] 30 AMP

- [ ] RESTROOMS
- [ ] SHOWERS
- [ ] LAUNDRY
- [ ] GENERATORS ALLOWED?
- [ ] PETS ALLOWED?
- [ ] PICNIC TABLE
- [ ] FIREPIT

- [ ] STORE ON SITE
- [ ] WHEELCHAIR ACCESSIBLE
- [ ] GROUP SITES
- [ ] SHADE
- [ ] FLAT SITES
- [ ] PULL THROUGH
- [ ] TRAIL ACCESS

NEARBY ATTRACTIONS

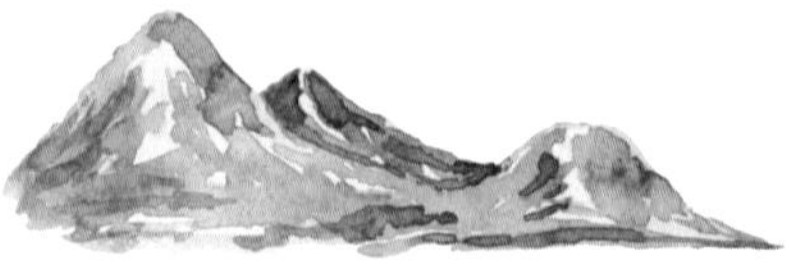

CAMPGROUND NOTES

>>>>>>>>>> MY FAVORITE MEMORY FROM THIS CAMP TRIP

NOTES TO REMEMBER FOR NEXT TIME

A PICTURE OR FUNNY STORY TO SMILE ABOUT LATER:

CAMPGROUND DETAILS

CAMPGROUND NAME

✗ LOCATION: _____

▭➔ DATES STAYED: _____

✳ SPOT NUMBER: _____

⭐ THE BEST SPOT # FOR NEXT TIME _____

COST PER NIGHT

✤ AVG. TEMPS _____

⟫⟫⟫⟫⟫ AMENITIES ⟪⟪⟪⟪⟪

☐ WATER
☐ SEWER HOOKUPS
☐ DUMP STATION
☐ CELL SERVICE
☐ WIFI AVAILABLE
☐ 15 AMP
☐ 30 AMP

☐ RESTROOMS
☐ SHOWERS
☐ LAUNDRY
☐ GENERATORS ALLOWED?
☐ PETS ALLOWED?
☐ PICNIC TABLE
☐ FIREPIT

☐ STORE ON SITE
☐ WHEELCHAIR ACCESSIBLE
☐ GROUP SITES
☐ SHADE
☐ FLAT SITES
☐ PULL THROUGH
☐ TRAIL ACCESS

NEARBY ATTRACTIONS

CAMPGROUND NOTES

>>>>>>>> MY FAVORITE MEMORY FROM THIS CAMP TRIP

NOTES TO REMEMBER FOR NEXT TIME

A PICTURE OR FUNNY STORY TO SMILE ABOUT LATER:

_____
_____
_____
_____
_____
_____
_____
_____
_____

CAMPGROUND DETAILS

CAMPGROUND NAME

LOCATION: _____

DATES STAYED: _____

SPOT NUMBER: _____

AVG. TEMPS _____

THE BEST SPOT # FOR NEXT TIME _____

COST PER NIGHT

>>>>>>>> AMENITIES <<<<<<<<

☐ WATER
☐ SEWER HOOKUPS
☐ DUMP STATION
☐ CELL SERVICE
☐ WIFI AVAILABLE
☐ 15 AMP
☐ 30 AMP

☐ RESTROOMS
☐ SHOWERS
☐ LAUNDRY
☐ GENERATORS ALLOWED?
☐ PETS ALLOWED?
☐ PICNIC TABLE
☐ FIREPIT

☐ STORE ON SITE
☐ WHEELCHAIR ACCESSIBLE
☐ GROUP SITES
☐ SHADE
☐ FLAT SITES
☐ PULL THROUGH
☐ TRAIL ACCESS

NEARBY ATTRACTIONS

CAMPGROUND NOTES

>>>>>>>>>> MY FAVORITE MEMORY FROM THIS CAMP TRIP

NOTES TO REMEMBER FOR NEXT TIME

A PICTURE OR FUNNY STORY TO SMILE ABOUT LATER:

CAMPGROUND DETAILS

CAMPGROUND NAME

❌ LOCATION: _____

▢➡ DATES STAYED: _____

✳ SPOT NUMBER: _____

✿ AVG. TEMPS _____

☆ THE BEST SPOT # FOR NEXT TIME _____

COST PER NIGHT

▶▶▶▶▶▶ AMENITIES ◀◀◀◀◀◀

☐ WATER
☐ SEWER HOOKUPS
☐ DUMP STATION
☐ CELL SERVICE
☐ WIFI AVAILABLE
☐ 15 AMP
☐ 30 AMP

☐ RESTROOMS
☐ SHOWERS
☐ LAUNDRY
☐ GENERATORS ALLOWED?
☐ PETS ALLOWED?
☐ PICNIC TABLE
☐ FIREPIT

☐ STORE ON SITE
☐ WHEELCHAIR ACCESSIBLE
☐ GROUP SITES
☐ SHADE
☐ FLAT SITES
☐ PULL THROUGH
☐ TRAIL ACCESS

NEARBY ATTRACTIONS ⇾

CAMPGROUND NOTES

>>>>>>>>>> MY FAVORITE MEMORY FROM THIS CAMP TRIP

NOTES TO REMEMBER FOR NEXT TIME

A PICTURE OR FUNNY STORY TO SMILE ABOUT LATER:

_____

_____

_____

_____

_____

_____

_____

_____

CAMPGROUND DETAILS

CAMPGROUND NAME

⊗ LOCATION: _____

▭➜ DATES STAYED: _____

✳ SPOT NUMBER: _____

✿ AVG. TEMPS _____

☆ THE BEST SPOT # FOR NEXT TIME _____

COST PER NIGHT

⫸⫸⫸ AMENITIES ⫷⫷⫷

- ☐ WATER
- ☐ SEWER HOOKUPS
- ☐ DUMP STATION
- ☐ CELL SERVICE
- ☐ WIFI AVAILABLE
- ☐ 15 AMP
- ☐ 30 AMP

- ☐ RESTROOMS
- ☐ SHOWERS
- ☐ LAUNDRY
- ☐ GENERATORS ALLOWED?
- ☐ PETS ALLOWED?
- ☐ PICNIC TABLE
- ☐ FIREPIT

- ☐ STORE ON SITE
- ☐ WHEELCHAIR ACCESSIBLE
- ☐ GROUP SITES
- ☐ SHADE
- ☐ FLAT SITES
- ☐ PULL THROUGH
- ☐ TRAIL ACCESS

NEARBY ATTRACTIONS ↘

CAMPGROUND NOTES

>>>>>>>>>>> MY FAVORITE MEMORY FROM THIS CAMP TRIP

NOTES TO REMEMBER FOR NEXT TIME

A PICTURE OR FUNNY STORY TO SMILE ABOUT LATER:

CAMPGROUND DETAILS

CAMPGROUND NAME

(×) LOCATION: _____

▢→ DATES STAYED: _____

(✳) SPOT NUMBER: _____

COST PER NIGHT

(✤) AVG. TEMPS _____

(★) THE BEST SPOT # FOR NEXT TIME _____

▶▶▶▶▶▶▶ AMENITIES ◀◀◀◀◀◀◀

☐ WATER
☐ SEWER HOOKUPS
☐ DUMP STATION
☐ CELL SERVICE
☐ WIFI AVAILABLE
☐ 15 AMP
☐ 30 AMP

☐ RESTROOMS
☐ SHOWERS
☐ LAUNDRY
☐ GENERATORS ALLOWED?
☐ PETS ALLOWED?
☐ PICNIC TABLE
☐ FIREPIT

☐ STORE ON SITE
☐ WHEELCHAIR ACCESSIBLE
☐ GROUP SITES
☐ SHADE
☐ FLAT SITES
☐ PULL THROUGH
☐ TRAIL ACCESS

NEARBY ATTRACTIONS ⇶↘

CAMPGROUND NOTES

>>>>>>>>>> MY FAVORITE MEMORY FROM THIS CAMP TRIP

NOTES TO REMEMBER FOR NEXT TIME

A PICTURE OR FUNNY STORY TO SMILE ABOUT LATER:

_____

_____

_____

_____

_____

_____

_____

_____

CAMPGROUND DETAILS

CAMPGROUND NAME

⊗ LOCATION: _____

▢→ DATES STAYED: _____

✳ SPOT NUMBER: _____

❀ AVG. TEMPS _____

COST PER NIGHT

☆ THE BEST SPOT # FOR NEXT TIME _____

▶▶▶▶▶▶▶ AMENITIES ◀◀◀◀◀◀◀

☐ WATER
☐ SEWER HOOKUPS
☐ DUMP STATION
☐ CELL SERVICE
☐ WIFI AVAILABLE
☐ 15 AMP
☐ 30 AMP

☐ RESTROOMS
☐ SHOWERS
☐ LAUNDRY
☐ GENERATORS ALLOWED?
☐ PETS ALLOWED?
☐ PICNIC TABLE
☐ FIREPIT

☐ STORE ON SITE
☐ WHEELCHAIR ACCESSIBLE
☐ GROUP SITES
☐ SHADE
☐ FLAT SITES
☐ PULL THROUGH
☐ TRAIL ACCESS

NEARBY ATTRACTIONS ⇾

CAMPGROUND NOTES

>>>>>>>>>> MY FAVORITE MEMORY FROM THIS CAMP TRIP

NOTES TO REMEMBER FOR NEXT TIME

A PICTURE OR FUNNY STORY TO SMILE ABOUT LATER:

_____
_____
_____
_____
_____
_____
_____
_____

CAMPGROUND DETAILS

CAMPGROUND NAME

⊗ LOCATION: _____

▭→ DATES STAYED: _____

✳ SPOT NUMBER: _____

✿ AVG. TEMPS _____

☆ THE BEST SPOT # FOR NEXT TIME _____

COST PER NIGHT

⟫⟫⟫⟫ AMENITIES ⟪⟪⟪⟪

☐ WATER
☐ SEWER HOOKUPS
☐ DUMP STATION
☐ CELL SERVICE
☐ WIFI AVAILABLE
☐ 15 AMP
☐ 30 AMP

☐ RESTROOMS
☐ SHOWERS
☐ LAUNDRY
☐ GENERATORS ALLOWED?
☐ PETS ALLOWED?
☐ PICNIC TABLE
☐ FIREPIT

☐ STORE ON SITE
☐ WHEELCHAIR ACCESSIBLE
☐ GROUP SITES
☐ SHADE
☐ FLAT SITES
☐ PULL THROUGH
☐ TRAIL ACCESS

NEARBY ATTRACTIONS →

CAMPGROUND NOTES

>>>>>>>>> MY FAVORITE MEMORY FROM THIS CAMP TRIP

NOTES TO REMEMBER FOR NEXT TIME

A PICTURE OR FUNNY STORY TO SMILE ABOUT LATER:

CAMPGROUND DETAILS

CAMPGROUND NAME

✖ LOCATION: _____

➡ DATES STAYED: _____

✳ SPOT NUMBER: _____

✿ AVG. TEMPS _____

☆ THE BEST SPOT # FOR NEXT TIME _____

COST PER NIGHT

▶▶▶▶▶▶ AMENITIES ◀◀◀◀◀◀◀◀

- ☐ WATER
- ☐ SEWER HOOKUPS
- ☐ DUMP STATION
- ☐ CELL SERVICE
- ☐ WIFI AVAILABLE
- ☐ 15 AMP
- ☐ 30 AMP

- ☐ RESTROOMS
- ☐ SHOWERS
- ☐ LAUNDRY
- ☐ GENERATORS ALLOWED?
- ☐ PETS ALLOWED?
- ☐ PICNIC TABLE
- ☐ FIREPIT

- ☐ STORE ON SITE
- ☐ WHEELCHAIR ACCESSIBLE
- ☐ GROUP SITES
- ☐ SHADE
- ☐ FLAT SITES
- ☐ PULL THROUGH
- ☐ TRAIL ACCESS

NEARBY ATTRACTIONS ↝

CAMPGROUND NOTES

>>>>>>>>> MY FAVORITE MEMORY FROM THIS CAMP TRIP

NOTES TO REMEMBER FOR NEXT TIME

A PICTURE OR FUNNY STORY TO SMILE ABOUT LATER:

_____
_____
_____
_____
_____
_____
_____
_____

CAMPGROUND DETAILS

CAMPGROUND NAME

❌ LOCATION: _____

⬛➡ DATES STAYED: _____

✳ SPOT NUMBER: _____

✤ AVG. TEMPS _____

☆ THE BEST SPOT # FOR NEXT TIME _____

COST PER NIGHT

▶▶▶▶▶ AMENITIES ◀◀◀◀◀◀

- ☐ WATER
- ☐ SEWER HOOKUPS
- ☐ DUMP STATION
- ☐ CELL SERVICE
- ☐ WIFI AVAILABLE
- ☐ 15 AMP
- ☐ 30 AMP

- ☐ RESTROOMS
- ☐ SHOWERS
- ☐ LAUNDRY
- ☐ GENERATORS ALLOWED?
- ☐ PETS ALLOWED?
- ☐ PICNIC TABLE
- ☐ FIREPIT

- ☐ STORE ON SITE
- ☐ WHEELCHAIR ACCESSIBLE
- ☐ GROUP SITES
- ☐ SHADE
- ☐ FLAT SITES
- ☐ PULL THROUGH
- ☐ TRAIL ACCESS

NEARBY ATTRACTIONS ⤳

CAMPGROUND NOTES

>>>>>>>>>> MY FAVORITE MEMORY FROM THIS CAMP TRIP

NOTES TO REMEMBER FOR NEXT TIME

A PICTURE OR FUNNY STORY TO SMILE ABOUT LATER:

CAMPGROUND DETAILS

CAMPGROUND NAME

✕ LOCATION: _____

⬛➡ DATES STAYED: _____

✳ SPOT NUMBER: _____

COST PER NIGHT

✿ AVG. TEMPS _____

☆ THE BEST SPOT # FOR NEXT TIME _____

▶▶▶▶▶▶ AMENITIES ◀◀◀◀◀◀

☐ WATER
☐ SEWER HOOKUPS
☐ DUMP STATION
☐ CELL SERVICE
☐ WIFI AVAILABLE
☐ 15 AMP
☐ 30 AMP

☐ RESTROOMS
☐ SHOWERS
☐ LAUNDRY
☐ GENERATORS ALLOWED?
☐ PETS ALLOWED?
☐ PICNIC TABLE
☐ FIREPIT

☐ STORE ON SITE
☐ WHEELCHAIR ACCESSIBLE
☐ GROUP SITES
☐ SHADE
☐ FLAT SITES
☐ PULL THROUGH
☐ TRAIL ACCESS

NEARBY ATTRACTIONS ↬

CAMPGROUND NOTES

>>>>>>>>>> *MY FAVORITE MEMORY FROM THIS CAMP TRIP*

NOTES TO REMEMBER FOR NEXT TIME

A PICTURE OR FUNNY STORY TO SMILE ABOUT LATER:

_____

_____

_____

_____

_____

_____

_____

_____

CAMPGROUND DETAILS

CAMPGROUND NAME

⊗ LOCATION: _____

⬛→ DATES STAYED: _____

✳ SPOT NUMBER: _____

☆ THE BEST SPOT # FOR NEXT TIME _____

COST PER NIGHT

✿ AVG. TEMPS _____

▶▶▶▶▶▶▶ AMENITIES ◀◀◀◀◀◀◀

☐ WATER
☐ SEWER HOOKUPS
☐ DUMP STATION
☐ CELL SERVICE
☐ WIFI AVAILABLE
☐ 15 AMP
☐ 30 AMP

☐ RESTROOMS
☐ SHOWERS
☐ LAUNDRY
☐ GENERATORS ALLOWED?
☐ PETS ALLOWED?
☐ PICNIC TABLE
☐ FIREPIT

☐ STORE ON SITE
☐ WHEELCHAIR ACCESSIBLE
☐ GROUP SITES
☐ SHADE
☐ FLAT SITES
☐ PULL THROUGH
☐ TRAIL ACCESS

NEARBY ATTRACTIONS ⇢

CAMPGROUND NOTES

>>>>>>>>>>> MY FAVORITE MEMORY FROM THIS CAMP TRIP

NOTES TO REMEMBER FOR NEXT TIME

A PICTURE OR FUNNY STORY TO SMILE ABOUT LATER:

CAMPGROUND DETAILS

CAMPGROUND NAME

(x) LOCATION: _____

COST PER NIGHT

☐→ DATES STAYED: _____

✳ SPOT NUMBER: _____   ✤ AVG. TEMPS _____

☆ THE BEST SPOT # FOR NEXT TIME _____

>>>>>>> AMENITIES <<<<<<<

☐ WATER
☐ SEWER HOOKUPS
☐ DUMP STATION
☐ CELL SERVICE
☐ WIFI AVAILABLE
☐ 15 AMP
☐ 30 AMP

☐ RESTROOMS
☐ SHOWERS
☐ LAUNDRY
☐ GENERATORS ALLOWED?
☐ PETS ALLOWED?
☐ PICNIC TABLE
☐ FIREPIT

☐ STORE ON SITE
☐ WHEELCHAIR ACCESSIBLE
☐ GROUP SITES
☐ SHADE
☐ FLAT SITES
☐ PULL THROUGH
☐ TRAIL ACCESS

NEARBY ATTRACTIONS ↗

CAMPGROUND NOTES

>>>>>>>>>> MY FAVORITE MEMORY FROM THIS CAMP TRIP

NOTES TO REMEMBER FOR NEXT TIME

A PICTURE OR FUNNY STORY TO SMILE ABOUT LATER:

_____

_____

_____

_____

_____

_____

_____

_____

CAMPGROUND DETAILS

CAMPGROUND NAME

(X) LOCATION: _____

☐→ DATES STAYED: _____

COST PER NIGHT

✳ SPOT NUMBER: _____   ✤ AVG. TEMPS _____

☆ THE BEST SPOT # FOR NEXT TIME _____

»»»»» AMENITIES «««««

☐ WATER
☐ SEWER HOOKUPS
☐ DUMP STATION
☐ CELL SERVICE
☐ WIFI AVAILABLE
☐ 15 AMP
☐ 30 AMP

☐ RESTROOMS
☐ SHOWERS
☐ LAUNDRY
☐ GENERATORS ALLOWED?
☐ PETS ALLOWED?
☐ PICNIC TABLE
☐ FIREPIT

☐ STORE ON SITE
☐ WHEELCHAIR ACCESSIBLE
☐ GROUP SITES
☐ SHADE
☐ FLAT SITES
☐ PULL THROUGH
☐ TRAIL ACCESS

NEARBY ATTRACTIONS ↦

CAMPGROUND NOTES

>>>>>>>>>> MY FAVORITE MEMORY FROM THIS CAMP TRIP

NOTES TO REMEMBER FOR NEXT TIME

A PICTURE OR FUNNY STORY TO SMILE ABOUT LATER:

_____

_____

_____

_____

_____

_____

_____

_____

CAMPGROUND DETAILS

CAMPGROUND NAME

⊗ LOCATION: _____

⬜→ DATES STAYED: _____

✳ SPOT NUMBER: _____

✿ AVG. TEMPS _____

☆ THE BEST SPOT # FOR NEXT TIME _____

COST PER NIGHT

⟫⟫⟫ AMENITIES ⟪⟪⟪

- ☐ WATER
- ☐ SEWER HOOKUPS
- ☐ DUMP STATION
- ☐ CELL SERVICE
- ☐ WIFI AVAILABLE
- ☐ 15 AMP
- ☐ 30 AMP

- ☐ RESTROOMS
- ☐ SHOWERS
- ☐ LAUNDRY
- ☐ GENERATORS ALLOWED?
- ☐ PETS ALLOWED?
- ☐ PICNIC TABLE
- ☐ FIREPIT

- ☐ STORE ON SITE
- ☐ WHEELCHAIR ACCESSIBLE
- ☐ GROUP SITES
- ☐ SHADE
- ☐ FLAT SITES
- ☐ PULL THROUGH
- ☐ TRAIL ACCESS

NEARBY ATTRACTIONS ↗

CAMPGROUND NOTES

>>>>>>>>>> MY FAVORITE MEMORY FROM THIS CAMP TRIP

NOTES TO REMEMBER FOR NEXT TIME

A PICTURE OR FUNNY STORY TO SMILE ABOUT LATER:

CAMPGROUND DETAILS

CAMPGROUND NAME

⊗ LOCATION: _____

COST PER NIGHT

⬛→ DATES STAYED: _____

✳ SPOT NUMBER: _____

❀ AVG. TEMPS _____

☆ THE BEST SPOT # FOR NEXT TIME _____

▶▶▶▶▶ AMENITIES ◀◀◀◀◀

- ☐ WATER
- ☐ SEWER HOOKUPS
- ☐ DUMP STATION
- ☐ CELL SERVICE
- ☐ WIFI AVAILABLE
- ☐ 15 AMP
- ☐ 30 AMP

- ☐ RESTROOMS
- ☐ SHOWERS
- ☐ LAUNDRY
- ☐ GENERATORS ALLOWED?
- ☐ PETS ALLOWED?
- ☐ PICNIC TABLE
- ☐ FIREPIT

- ☐ STORE ON SITE
- ☐ WHEELCHAIR ACCESSIBLE
- ☐ GROUP SITES
- ☐ SHADE
- ☐ FLAT SITES
- ☐ PULL THROUGH
- ☐ TRAIL ACCESS

NEARBY ATTRACTIONS ↘

CAMPGROUND NOTES

>>>>>>>>> MY FAVORITE MEMORY FROM THIS CAMP TRIP

NOTES TO REMEMBER FOR NEXT TIME

A PICTURE OR FUNNY STORY TO SMILE ABOUT LATER:

CAMPGROUND DETAILS

CAMPGROUND NAME

✖ LOCATION: _____

⬅ DATES STAYED: _____

✳ SPOT NUMBER: _____

❀ AVG. TEMPS _____

⭐ THE BEST SPOT # FOR NEXT TIME _____

COST PER NIGHT

▶▶▶▶▶ AMENITIES ◀◀◀◀◀

- ☐ WATER
- ☐ SEWER HOOKUPS
- ☐ DUMP STATION
- ☐ CELL SERVICE
- ☐ WIFI AVAILABLE
- ☐ 15 AMP
- ☐ 30 AMP

- ☐ RESTROOMS
- ☐ SHOWERS
- ☐ LAUNDRY
- ☐ GENERATORS ALLOWED?
- ☐ PETS ALLOWED?
- ☐ PICNIC TABLE
- ☐ FIREPIT

- ☐ STORE ON SITE
- ☐ WHEELCHAIR ACCESSIBLE
- ☐ GROUP SITES
- ☐ SHADE
- ☐ FLAT SITES
- ☐ PULL THROUGH
- ☐ TRAIL ACCESS

NEARBY ATTRACTIONS ⇀

CAMPGROUND NOTES

>>>>>>>>>>> MY FAVORITE MEMORY FROM THIS CAMP TRIP

NOTES TO REMEMBER FOR NEXT TIME

A PICTURE OR FUNNY STORY TO SMILE ABOUT LATER:

_____

_____

_____

_____

_____

_____

_____

_____

_____

CAMPGROUND DETAILS

CAMPGROUND NAME

✕ LOCATION: _____

⬛➡ DATES STAYED: _____

✳ SPOT NUMBER: _____

COST PER NIGHT

✿ AVG. TEMPS _____

☆ THE BEST SPOT # FOR NEXT TIME _____

▶▶▶▶▶▶ AMENITIES ◀◀◀◀◀◀

☐ WATER
☐ SEWER HOOKUPS
☐ DUMP STATION
☐ CELL SERVICE
☐ WIFI AVAILABLE
☐ 15 AMP
☐ 30 AMP

☐ RESTROOMS
☐ SHOWERS
☐ LAUNDRY
☐ GENERATORS ALLOWED?
☐ PETS ALLOWED?
☐ PICNIC TABLE
☐ FIREPIT

☐ STORE ON SITE
☐ WHEELCHAIR ACCESSIBLE
☐ GROUP SITES
☐ SHADE
☐ FLAT SITES
☐ PULL THROUGH
☐ TRAIL ACCESS

NEARBY ATTRACTIONS ↘

CAMPGROUND NOTES

>>>>>>>>> *MY FAVORITE MEMORY FROM THIS CAMP TRIP*

NOTES TO REMEMBER FOR NEXT TIME

A PICTURE OR FUNNY STORY TO SMILE ABOUT LATER:

_____
_____
_____
_____
_____
_____
_____
_____

CAMPGROUND DETAILS

CAMPGROUND NAME

LOCATION: _____

DATES STAYED: _____

SPOT NUMBER: _____

COST PER NIGHT

AVG. TEMPS _____

THE BEST SPOT # FOR NEXT TIME _____

AMENITIES

- ☐ WATER
- ☐ SEWER HOOKUPS
- ☐ DUMP STATION
- ☐ CELL SERVICE
- ☐ WIFI AVAILABLE
- ☐ 15 AMP
- ☐ 30 AMP

- ☐ RESTROOMS
- ☐ SHOWERS
- ☐ LAUNDRY
- ☐ GENERATORS ALLOWED?
- ☐ PETS ALLOWED?
- ☐ PICNIC TABLE
- ☐ FIREPIT

- ☐ STORE ON SITE
- ☐ WHEELCHAIR ACCESSIBLE
- ☐ GROUP SITES
- ☐ SHADE
- ☐ FLAT SITES
- ☐ PULL THROUGH
- ☐ TRAIL ACCESS

NEARBY ATTRACTIONS

CAMPGROUND NOTES

>>>>>>>> MY FAVORITE MEMORY FROM THIS CAMP TRIP

NOTES TO REMEMBER FOR NEXT TIME

A PICTURE OR FUNNY STORY TO SMILE ABOUT LATER:

CAMPGROUND DETAILS

CAMPGROUND NAME

(×) LOCATION: _____

☐→ DATES STAYED: _____

(✳) SPOT NUMBER: _____

⊕ AVG. TEMPS _____

COST PER NIGHT

(☆) THE BEST SPOT # FOR NEXT TIME _____

▶▶▶▶▶▶▶ AMENITIES ◀◀◀◀◀◀◀

☐ WATER
☐ SEWER HOOKUPS
☐ DUMP STATION
☐ CELL SERVICE
☐ WIFI AVAILABLE
☐ 15 AMP
☐ 30 AMP

☐ RESTROOMS
☐ SHOWERS
☐ LAUNDRY
☐ GENERATORS ALLOWED?
☐ PETS ALLOWED?
☐ PICNIC TABLE
☐ FIREPIT

☐ STORE ON SITE
☐ WHEELCHAIR ACCESSIBLE
☐ GROUP SITES
☐ SHADE
☐ FLAT SITES
☐ PULL THROUGH
☐ TRAIL ACCESS

NEARBY ATTRACTIONS ➤

CAMPGROUND NOTES

>>>>>>>> MY FAVORITE MEMORY FROM THIS CAMP TRIP

NOTES TO REMEMBER FOR NEXT TIME

A PICTURE OR FUNNY STORY TO SMILE ABOUT LATER:

CAMPGROUND DETAILS

CAMPGROUND NAME

✖ LOCATION: _____

COST PER NIGHT

▢➡ DATES STAYED: _____

✳ SPOT NUMBER: _____   ❀ AVG. TEMPS _____

★ THE BEST SPOT # FOR NEXT TIME _____

▶▶▶ AMENITIES ◀◀◀

☐ WATER
☐ SEWER HOOKUPS
☐ DUMP STATION
☐ CELL SERVICE
☐ WIFI AVAILABLE
☐ 15 AMP
☐ 30 AMP

☐ RESTROOMS
☐ SHOWERS
☐ LAUNDRY
☐ GENERATORS ALLOWED?
☐ PETS ALLOWED?
☐ PICNIC TABLE
☐ FIREPIT

☐ STORE ON SITE
☐ WHEELCHAIR ACCESSIBLE
☐ GROUP SITES
☐ SHADE
☐ FLAT SITES
☐ PULL THROUGH
☐ TRAIL ACCESS

NEARBY ATTRACTIONS ↘

CAMPGROUND NOTES

>>>>>>>>>> MY FAVORITE MEMORY FROM THIS CAMP TRIP

NOTES TO REMEMBER FOR NEXT TIME

A PICTURE OR FUNNY STORY TO SMILE ABOUT LATER:

CAMPGROUND DETAILS

CAMPGROUND NAME

LOCATION: ____________________

DATES STAYED: ____________________

COST PER NIGHT

SPOT NUMBER: ____________

AVG. TEMPS ____________

THE BEST SPOT # FOR NEXT TIME ____________________

AMENITIES

- ☐ WATER
- ☐ SEWER HOOKUPS
- ☐ DUMP STATION
- ☐ CELL SERVICE
- ☐ WIFI AVAILABLE
- ☐ 15 AMP
- ☐ 30 AMP
- ☐ RESTROOMS
- ☐ SHOWERS
- ☐ LAUNDRY
- ☐ GENERATORS ALLOWED?
- ☐ PETS ALLOWED?
- ☐ PICNIC TABLE
- ☐ FIREPIT
- ☐ STORE ON SITE
- ☐ WHEELCHAIR ACCESSIBLE
- ☐ GROUP SITES
- ☐ SHADE
- ☐ FLAT SITES
- ☐ PULL THROUGH
- ☐ TRAIL ACCESS

NEARBY ATTRACTIONS

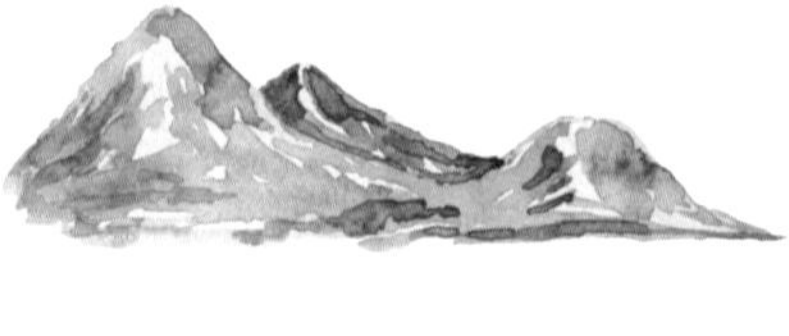

CAMPGROUND NOTES

>>>>>>>>>> MY FAVORITE MEMORY FROM THIS CAMP TRIP

NOTES TO REMEMBER FOR NEXT TIME

A PICTURE OR FUNNY STORY TO SMILE ABOUT LATER:

CAMPGROUND DETAILS

CAMPGROUND NAME

(×) LOCATION: _____

➡ DATES STAYED: _____

COST PER NIGHT

(✳) SPOT NUMBER: _____ (✿) AVG. TEMPS _____

(★) THE BEST SPOT # FOR NEXT TIME _____

▶▶▶▶▶▶▶ AMENITIES ◀◀◀◀◀◀◀

☐ WATER
☐ SEWER HOOKUPS
☐ DUMP STATION
☐ CELL SERVICE
☐ WIFI AVAILABLE
☐ 15 AMP
☐ 30 AMP

☐ RESTROOMS
☐ SHOWERS
☐ LAUNDRY
☐ GENERATORS ALLOWED?
☐ PETS ALLOWED?
☐ PICNIC TABLE
☐ FIREPIT

☐ STORE ON SITE
☐ WHEELCHAIR ACCESSIBLE
☐ GROUP SITES
☐ SHADE
☐ FLAT SITES
☐ PULL THROUGH
☐ TRAIL ACCESS

NEARBY ATTRACTIONS ↬

CAMPGROUND NOTES

>>>>>>>>> MY FAVORITE MEMORY FROM THIS CAMP TRIP

NOTES TO REMEMBER FOR NEXT TIME

A PICTURE OR FUNNY STORY TO SMILE ABOUT LATER:

CAMPGROUND DETAILS

CAMPGROUND NAME

ⓧ LOCATION: _____

▭➡ DATES STAYED: _____

✳ SPOT NUMBER: _____   ✤ AVG. TEMPS _____

COST PER NIGHT

☆ THE BEST SPOT # FOR NEXT TIME _____

▶▶▶▶▶ AMENITIES ◀◀◀◀◀◀

☐ WATER
☐ SEWER HOOKUPS
☐ DUMP STATION
☐ CELL SERVICE
☐ WIFI AVAILABLE
☐ 15 AMP
☐ 30 AMP

☐ RESTROOMS
☐ SHOWERS
☐ LAUNDRY
☐ GENERATORS ALLOWED?
☐ PETS ALLOWED?
☐ PICNIC TABLE
☐ FIREPIT

☐ STORE ON SITE
☐ WHEELCHAIR ACCESSIBLE
☐ GROUP SITES
☐ SHADE
☐ FLAT SITES
☐ PULL THROUGH
☐ TRAIL ACCESS

NEARBY ATTRACTIONS ➤

CAMPGROUND NOTES

>>>>>>>>>> MY FAVORITE MEMORY FROM THIS CAMP TRIP

NOTES TO REMEMBER FOR NEXT TIME

A PICTURE OR FUNNY STORY TO SMILE ABOUT LATER:

_____

_____

_____

_____

_____

_____

_____

_____

CAMPGROUND DETAILS

CAMPGROUND NAME

LOCATION: _____

COST PER NIGHT

DATES STAYED: _____

SPOT NUMBER: _____ AVG. TEMPS _____

THE BEST SPOT # FOR NEXT TIME _____

AMENITIES

- ☐ WATER
- ☐ SEWER HOOKUPS
- ☐ DUMP STATION
- ☐ CELL SERVICE
- ☐ WIFI AVAILABLE
- ☐ 15 AMP
- ☐ 30 AMP

- ☐ RESTROOMS
- ☐ SHOWERS
- ☐ LAUNDRY
- ☐ GENERATORS ALLOWED?
- ☐ PETS ALLOWED?
- ☐ PICNIC TABLE
- ☐ FIREPIT

- ☐ STORE ON SITE
- ☐ WHEELCHAIR ACCESSIBLE
- ☐ GROUP SITES
- ☐ SHADE
- ☐ FLAT SITES
- ☐ PULL THROUGH
- ☐ TRAIL ACCESS

NEARBY ATTRACTIONS

CAMPGROUND NOTES

>>>>>>>>> MY FAVORITE MEMORY FROM THIS CAMP TRIP

NOTES TO REMEMBER FOR NEXT TIME

A PICTURE OR FUNNY STORY TO SMILE ABOUT LATER:

CAMPGROUND DETAILS

CAMPGROUND NAME

⊗ LOCATION: _____

▭→ DATES STAYED: _____

❋ SPOT NUMBER: _____

✪ THE BEST SPOT # FOR NEXT TIME _____

COST PER NIGHT

✿ AVG. TEMPS _____

≫≫≫ AMENITIES ≪≪≪

- ☐ WATER
- ☐ SEWER HOOKUPS
- ☐ DUMP STATION
- ☐ CELL SERVICE
- ☐ WIFI AVAILABLE
- ☐ 15 AMP
- ☐ 30 AMP

- ☐ RESTROOMS
- ☐ SHOWERS
- ☐ LAUNDRY
- ☐ GENERATORS ALLOWED?
- ☐ PETS ALLOWED?
- ☐ PICNIC TABLE
- ☐ FIREPIT

- ☐ STORE ON SITE
- ☐ WHEELCHAIR ACCESSIBLE
- ☐ GROUP SITES
- ☐ SHADE
- ☐ FLAT SITES
- ☐ PULL THROUGH
- ☐ TRAIL ACCESS

NEARBY ATTRACTIONS ↝

CAMPGROUND NOTES

>>>>>>>>> MY FAVORITE MEMORY FROM THIS CAMP TRIP

NOTES TO REMEMBER FOR NEXT TIME

A PICTURE OR FUNNY STORY TO SMILE ABOUT LATER:

_____
_____
_____
_____
_____
_____
_____
_____

DEPARTURE CHECKLIST

>>>>>>>>> BEFORE I GO··· <<<<<<<<<

- ☐ ROLL UP AWNING
- ☐ STOW OUTDOOR GEAR
- ☐ DISCONNECT SEWER HOSE
- ☐ UNPLUG POWER CORD
- ☐ DISCONNECT FRESH WATER
- ☐ TURN OFF ALL LIGHTS
- ☐ TURN OFF WATER PUMP
- ☐ TURN ALL PROPANE APPLIANCES OFF
- ☐ SHUT OFF PROPANE BOTTLE VALVE
- ☐ ENSURE FRIDGE IS RUNNING ON 12V DC/OFF
- ☐ STOW APPLIANCES
- ☐ LOWER TV ANTENNA
- ☐ CLOSE ROOF VENTS
- ☐ CLOSE ALL WINDOWS
- ☐ HITCH UP - MAKE SURE HITCH RECEIVER CLOSED
- ☐ PLUG IN UMBILICAL CORD (LIGHTS)
- ☐ RAISE JACKS
- ☐ STORE LEVELING BLOCKS
- ☐ CHECK ALL COMPARTMENTS LOCKED
- ☐ MOVE WHEELS OFF ANY LEVELING BLOCKS AND STORE
- ☐ ONE LAST CHECK FOR GEAR
- ☐ DOUBLE CHECK ALL TOW SAFETY DEVICES CORRECTLY USED

NOTES

TOOLS TO HAVE ON HAND

PREP FOR EVERYTHING!

- ☐ SCREWDRIVER W/MULTIPLE TIP SIZES
- ☐ NEEDLE NOSE PLIERS
- ☐ ELECTRICAL TAPE
- ☐ ZIP TIES
- ☐ DUCT TAPE
- ☐ HAMMER
- ☐ BUNGEE CORDS/RATCHET STRAP
- ☐ FOLDING SHOVEL
- ☐ SMALL STEP STOOL/LADDER
- ☐ EXTRA EXTENSION CORDS
- ☐ FLASHLIGHT
- ☐ EXTRA HITCH PIN
- ☐ EXTRA FRESH WATER CAP
- ☐ INEXPENSIVE MULTIMETER
- ☐ BATTERY TERMINAL CLEANER
- ☐ PORTABLE JUMP STARTER
- ☐ ELECTRONIC CONTACT CLEANER
- ☐ GORILLA GLUE

MORE "JUST IN CASE" ITEMS

INSURANCE CARD/ID/PHONE

⭐

PERSONAL ITEM PACKING LIST

THROW THESE IN THE BAG!

- [ ] SOAP AND SHAMPOO
- [ ] ALLERGY MEDICINE
- [ ] SUNSCREEN
- [ ] BUG SPRAY
- [ ] EYE DROPS
- [ ] FIRST AID KIT
- [ ] PRESCRIPTIONS
- [ ] IBUPROFEN
- [ ] FEMININE PRODUCTS

- [ ] GLASSES/CONTACTS
- [ ] TOOTHBRUSH & TOOTHPASTE
- [ ] LOTION
- [ ] NAIL CLIPPERS
- [ ] SUNGLASSES
- [ ] DEODORANT
- [ ] COMB/BRUSH
- [ ] RAZOR
- [ ] SHOWER SHOES

CAN'T FORGET THESE!

- ◯
- ◯
- ◯
- ◯
- ◯
- ◯

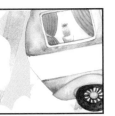

MY NOTES

JOT DOWN ANY THOUGHTS OR THINGS TO REMEMBER HERE!

MY NOTES

JOT DOWN ANY THOUGHTS OR THINGS TO REMEMBER HERE!

_____

_____

_____

_____

_____

_____

_____

_____

_____

_____

_____

_____

_____

_____

_____

_____

_____

_____

_____

_____

_____

_____

_____

MY NOTES

JOT DOWN ANY THOUGHTS OR THINGS TO REMEMBER HERE!

_____
_____
_____
_____
_____
_____
_____
_____
_____
_____
_____
_____
_____
_____
_____
_____
_____
_____
_____
_____
_____
_____

MY NOTES

JOT DOWN ANY THOUGHTS OR THINGS TO REMEMBER HERE!

MY NOTES

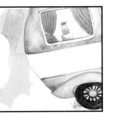

JOT DOWN ANY THOUGHTS OR THINGS TO REMEMBER HERE!

_____
_____
_____
_____
_____
_____
_____
_____
_____
_____
_____
_____
_____
_____
_____
_____
_____
_____
_____
_____

FAVORITE MEMORIES

PASTE IN SOME PICTURES OF YOUR FAVORITE MEMORIES HERE THAT
DON'T QUITE FIT INTO ANY OTHER CATEGORY!

FAVORITE MEMORIES

PASTE IN SOME PICTURES OF YOUR FAVORITE MEMORIES HERE THAT
DON'T QUITE FIT INTO ANY OTHER CATEGORY!

THANK YOU AGAIN!

I hope you have been enjoying your journal! If you're looking for more camping and outdoor tips, I highly encourage you to check out my website, thecrazyoutdoormama.com

Sign up at www.thecrazyoutdoormama.com/the-crazy-outdoor-mama-library/ to be added to my email list of thousands of others campers as well as get access to my library of free printables!

I have ALOT of kid themed camping/outdoor printables, so if you have kids or grandkids, you definitely gotta print a few off!

I will likely be publishing a kids camp games book in the future, so be on the lookout for that!

In the meantime, it would absolutely make my day if you could leave a review on Amazon with your thoughts! =)

Feel free to email me at thecrazyoutdoormama@gmail.com to ask any questions or for any collab ideas!

From my family to yours, I sincerely hope you make some amazing memories while out and about! And if you are ever near Jackson, Wyoming please email me - I'd love to meet ya!

Safe travels! <3,
Stacy